Common Core
Writing Companion

HIGH SCHOOL—Level B

Perfection Learning®

EDITORIAL DIRECTOR:	CAROL FRANCIS
EXECUTIVE EDITOR:	JIM STRICKLER
EDITOR:	ANDREA STARK
PROOFREADING COORDINATOR:	SHERI COOPER
ART DIRECTOR:	RANDY MESSER
DESIGNER:	TOBI CUNNINGHAM
COVER:	MIKE ASPENGREN

REVIEWERS:

MARCIA PUNSALAN
LANGUAGE DEPARTMENT CHAIR
CLAY HIGH SCHOOL
OREGON CITY SCHOOL DISTRICT
OREGON, OHIO

SHARON LINDELL-HOLZMAN
HALF HOLLOW HILLS HIGH SCHOOL EAST
HALF HOLLOW HILLS CENTRAL SCHOOL DISTRICT
NEW YORK

5 6 7 PP 18 17

94071

ISBN: 978-0-7891-8892-2

Printed in the United States of America

Common Core State Standards © Copyright 2010 by the National Governors Association
Center for Best Practices and Council of Chief State School Officers. All rights reserved.

• • • • • • • • • • • • • • Table of Contents • • • • • • • • • • • • • •

Table of Contents *continued*

Writing for College and Career

Congratulations! You've almost reached the end of your high school education. You have probably begun to think about what to do after you graduate. Your future plans may include attending a two- or four-year college, or you may plan to find a job. Whatever your plans are, you will need strong writing skills to be effective in your chosen path. This book will help you become a solid writer, one who can communicate your thoughts and ideas in a clear, concise way.

The activities in the book will also help prepare for writing tests. Whether taking the SAT, ACT, or graduation tests, you will be required to demonstrate that you can write effectively for a variety of purposes and tasks. The lessons in this book will prepare you to succeed on writing assessments.

What Are the Characteristics of Good Writing?

Your writing will be evaluated according to how well it shows the basic characteristics found in all types of good writing:

- *Development:* Does the text state the key idea clearly and support it strongly?
- *Organization:* Does the text include an introduction, body, and conclusion? Are transitions from one idea to another smooth and logical?
- *Evidence:* Is the information in the text relevant and strong?
- *Language and Style:* Does the text use words precisely? Is the tone appropriate?
- *Grammar, Spelling, and Punctuation:* Does the text use standard grammar, spelling, and punctuation?

How Is This Book Organized?

The first chapter of this book provides instruction and activities to help develop the characteristics of good writing listed above.

Each of the next five chapters focuses on a different type of writing.

- arguments
- informational/explanatory texts
- research reports
- literary analyses
- narratives

In each of these five chapters, the first several lessons highlight the elements particularly important to one type of writing. For example, the chapter on arguments includes lessons that focus on claims and counterclaims.

The next-to-last lesson in each chapter takes you, step by step, through writing a text. Built into these lessons are instruction and practice in grammar and usage that address the most common writing problems.

The final lesson in each chapter provides prompts for you to demonstrate your skills in gathering, analyzing, and using information in your writing. This lesson ends with a checklist based on the characteristics of good writing.

Chapter 1

Characteristics of Good Writing

Whether you are reporting on research or narrating your life story, good writing shares some common characteristics. Your writing will be evaluated on these qualities. Look for these elements on writing rubrics.

> **Good writing:**
> - is **well developed**
> - has **cohesive organization**
> - contains **evidence** from sources to support main points
> - uses **precise language** and a formal **style**
> - follows rules of **standard grammar, spelling,** and **punctuation**

LESSON 1 DEVELOPMENT

Well-developed writing focuses in on a main idea. This central idea is then expanded with interesting details, relevant facts, or carefully chosen evidence. Your writing should have a clear purpose that is appropriate to the task and the audience.

> **Purposes for Writing**
>
> Common writing purposes include informing, explaining, narrating a real or imagined story, and presenting an argument to convince readers.

Activity 1A Finding the Main Idea

Read the following paragraph and underline the main idea. Then answer the questions that follow.

> Students join the military for several different reasons. Some join up because they have a parent or a sibling already serving. Others like the idea of traveling around the world. But probably the most popular reasons to enlist are related to money. Many young people find that they can't get a job with merely a high school diploma. However, they also can't afford college. Joining the military can be a good solution for these problems. Enlistees get a steady income, while learning job skills. Plus the military has tuition assistance programs that help pay for college. Military service can be a good next step for some graduates.

1. What is the purpose of the passage?

_____

_____

2. How do the supporting details develop the main idea?

_____

_____

_____

_____

_____

3. Are the supporting details relevant and sufficient? If not, what details need to be added?

_____

_____

_____

_____

> **Relevant and Sufficient**
> ....
> • Relevant details relate to the main idea.
> • Sufficient details mean there are enough details to answer the main questions the reader has about the topic.

Activity 1B Writing a Paragraph

Read the following facts about the job market and college. Then complete the exercises that follow.

> ### 55 Million Good Reasons to Go to College
>
> *As college costs keep rising and student-loan debt causes national consternation, more Americans are asking whether young people should bother with college.*
>
> • The U.S. economy will generate 55 million job openings by 2020, according to the Georgetown University Center on Education and the Workforce, and 65 % of those jobs will require some training beyond a high-school education.
>
> • As the U.S. has moved from an industrial economy to one based more on knowledge, jobs have demanded greater levels of education. In 1973, according to the Georgetown Center, 72 % of jobs required a high-school education or less. In 2010, that figure was 41 %, and by 2020, it will have fallen to 36 %.
>
> • The Center has found that college graduates earn 84 % more over their lifetimes than people with only a high-school diploma, and that the gap will continue to widen.

continued on next page

continued from previous page

- Several organizations have shown that the majority of jobs created since the 2007–2009 recession have been low-skill, low-wage positions, primarily in fields such as retail sales, home healthcare and food service. A 2012 report from the National Employment Law Project, for example, found that 58% of the jobs added during the recovery were in categories like these.

Source: Weber, Lauren. 55 Million Good Reasons to Go to College. *The Wall Street Journal.* June 26, 2013. Web. 17 December 2013.

1. Use the text above as a source of information for a paragraph of your own. Write a main idea statement for your paragraph.

_____

_____

_____

> **Collaboration on Paragraphs**
>
> Use the following questions to evaluate a partner's paragraph: Is the purpose clear? Is the main idea well developed? Are there sufficient supporting details?

2. Go back to the passage and underline four details you can use to support your main idea statement.

3. Write a paragraph which will be read by your classmates. Be sure your paragraph includes both your main idea statement and good supporting details. Put the information in your own words. Do not merely copy sentences from the passage.

_____

_____

_____

_____

_____

_____

_____

_____

_____

LESSON 2 ORGANIZATION

Organize your writing to fit your purpose. Present details in a logical order so that the reader can follow the train of thought. Transitional words and phrases help the reader understand how ideas fit together cohesively, resulting in clear, unified writing.

> **Essay Organization**
>
> Most essays are organized using an introduction, a body, and a conclusion. The introduction and conclusion are one paragraph in length; the body is several paragraphs.

Organization	Use when your purpose is to	Transitional phrases
Chronological: time order	explain events (narrative writing)	*first, next, later, afterward, a few days later, at the same time*
	explain steps in a process (expository writing)	
Order of Importance: least to most important or most to least important	explain reasons (argumentative or persuasive writing)	*first, another reason, however, on the other hand, finally*
	explain procedures or rules (expository writing)	
Cause and Effect: explain the causes first and then the results	describe the relationship between causes and results (expository writing)	*as a result, for the reason that, because, as a result, since, due to the fact that*
Comparison and Contrast: group all similarities and all differences together or explain how each element is the same or different	show how things are alike and/ or different (expository writing)	*similarly, in the same way, on the other hand, but, conversely*

Activity 2A Analyzing a Paragraph

Read the passage. Then complete the exercises on the following page.

> Why is the cost of health care skyrocketing? There is no simple answer. A combination of factors has resulted in Americans paying more for quality health care. First, hospital mergers are increasing. Studies show that bigger hospitals have the power to exact higher fees from both insurance companies and patients. Another cause of rising health care costs is that more people suffer from chronic conditions such as diabetes, obesity, and heart disease. These conditions require more care over longer periods of time. Finally, medical technology also drives up costs. Newer procedures and equipment cost more than older technologies. While technology can speed a patient's recovery, physicians and hospitals often try to recoup the cost of new equipment by overprescribing these expensive procedures. In various ways, these factors continue to inflate the price tag of quality health care in the United States.

1. Underline the main idea of the paragraph on page 9.

2. How are the main points organized? Refer to the chart on page 9 for organizational structures.

_____

3. Circle three transitional words or phrases that help the reader make connections between the ideas.

Activity 2B Writing a Paragraph

Read the following facts about community service, or service learning, that is required for graduation. Then write a paragraph arguing for or against such requirements. Organize your paragraph logically. Use good transitional phrases. Use another piece of paper, if needed.

- In Maryland, where students must complete 75 hours of service learning, volunteering increased among 8th graders, but eventually decreased among older students.

- Service learning teaches students how to be good citizens and members of the community.

- Volunteering teaches valuable life skills and may lead to part-time work or a future career.

- Some students question whether compulsory public service was really "volunteering."

- One Canadian study found that students who completed more than the required hours were actively volunteering before the mandate was in place.

Collaboration on Organization

Use the following questions to evaluate a partner's paragraph:

- Is the organization of the paragraph clear?

- Are appropriate transitional words and phrases used to connect ideas?

- Do the ideas flow in logical order? Give your partner specific suggestions of how he or she can improve the organization of the paragraph. Revise your own paragraph based upon your partner's evaluation.

_____

_____

_____

_____

_____

_____

_____

LESSON 3 EVIDENCE

Often a prompt will ask you to develop your essay by providing textual evidence. **Textual evidence** includes direct quotations and references to specific information found in the reading. Gather evidence by reading texts closely and drawing information from them.

Activity 3A Analyzing a Paragraph

Read the following paragraph. Then complete the exercises below.

In his Civil Rights Address, President Kennedy gives a picture of what conditions were like for African Americans in the summer of 1963. "The Negro baby born in America today, regardless of the section of the State in which he is born, has about one-half as much chance of completing high school as a white baby born in the same place on the same day." Kennedy states that because of poor educational opportunities, African Americans were earning about half as much as whites earned. And if they were somehow able to survive on their meager wages, Blacks were still not free to eat lunch in a restaurant or vote for public officials. Kennedy laments that "One hundred years of delay have passed since President Lincoln freed the slaves, yet their heirs, their grandsons are not fully free."

1. Underline three examples of textual evidence.

2. Is there adequate textual evidence to support the main idea? Why or why not?

_____

_____

_____

_____

_____

_____

_____

_____

Close Reading

Interacting with what you read helps you understand and remember it. Develop the habit of identifying key ideas and terms as you read. Beyond that, look for patterns in the text and ask questions. Jot down comments that help you connect the content to other texts or ideas.

When reading printed materials you own, underline text and make notes in the margin. For materials you do not own and for online texts that you cannot write on directly, write notes on another sheet of paper or type them into a computer file.

Activity 3B Writing a Paragraph

Read the following passage. Then follow the directions below.

> The fires of frustration and discord are burning in every city, North and South, where legal remedies are not at hand. Redress is sought in the streets, in demonstrations, parades, and protests which create tensions and threaten violence and threaten lives.
>
> We face, therefore, a moral crisis as a country and a people. It cannot be met by repressive police action. It cannot be left to increased demonstrations in the streets. It cannot be quieted by token moves or talk. It is a time to act in the Congress, in your State and local legislative body and, above all, in all of our daily lives. It is not enough to pin the blame on others, to say this a problem of one section of the country or another, or deplore the facts that we face. A great change is at hand, and our task, our obligation, is to make that revolution, that change, peaceful and constructive for all. Those who do nothing are inviting shame, as well as violence. Those who act boldly are recognizing right, as well as reality.
>
> —President John F. Kennedy,
> Civil Rights Address, June 11, 1963

Write a paragraph describing how President Kennedy wants Americans to bring about changes in civil rights. Support your ideas using evidence from the passage above.

_____

_____

_____

_____

_____

_____

_____

_____

_____

_____

Collaboration on Evidence

Use the following questions to evaluate a partner's paragraph:

- Does the paragraph use evidence from the text?

- Is the evidence the strongest support for your points?

- Does the paragraph reinforce the writer's ideas?

- Be specific as you answer these questions. Revise your paragraph based on your partner's evaluation.

LESSON 4 LANGUAGE AND STYLE

Good writing uses **language** that is precise and clear. Words are carefully chosen to help the reader "see" what is being described. Verbs are mostly active voice; nouns are specific. The **style** of the writing is formal, avoiding slang and personal pronouns. Sentences vary in length and structure to draw the reader into the writing.

> ### Figurative Language
>
> Most writers rely on similes and metaphors when writing poetry or stories. However, figurative language can also be used in informative writing to make complex ideas clear.

Activity 4A Analyzing a Paragraph

Read the following paragraph and underline three examples of clear, precise language. Identify one example of figurative language.

> Once, a traveler driving through northwestern Iowa surveyed only endless fields of corn and soybeans—an unbroken sea of green. Nowadays, these fields are dominated by massive white wind turbines, towering up to 20 stories high like giant airplane propellers. Many farmers are happy to partner with wind energy companies that pay for renting a small quilt block of their land. And since wind energy is essentially free once the turbine is in place, more farmers are expected to harvest wind energy as they raise crops.

Activity 4B Writing a Paragraph

Choose a topic you have studied recently in another class. Write a paragraph that demonstrates clear, precise language and formal style.

> ### Collaboration on Evaluation
>
> Use the following to evaluate a partner's paragraph:
>
> - Can you identify four or more examples of precise language?
> - Does the writing include interesting comparisons or figurative language?
> - Does it use a formal style and objective tone? Revise your paragraphs on the basis of your partner's and your own evaluation.

_____

_____

_____

_____

_____

_____

_____

_____

_____

LESSON 5 CONVENTIONS IN WRITING

You may not be overly concerned about using correct **grammar, spelling,** and **punctuation** when sending a text or e-mail to a friend. However, these things do matter to employers and professors. Incorrect spelling, lack of capital letters and punctuation, or using wrong forms of words confuses your message. Mistakes also imply that you don't know the rules of formal English, or that you don't care enough to proofread your writing.

Activity 5A Editing a Paragraph

Edit the paragraph for mistakes in grammar, spelling, and punctuation by rewriting it correctly on the lines below.

> On weekends, families used to go out together to restaurants movie theaters and sporting events. Thanks to wireless Internet mega-size televisions, and lifelike video games, more americans are staying in. Trend forecasters called this behavior "cocooning." Streaming movies and to watch sporting events in high definition is more convenint than sitting in a crowded theater or stadium. Why drive over to a friends house to hang out when you can Facebook them or play online video games together. Faith Popcorn, a trend forecaster, "I think were looking for protection. Almost like the Jetsons we want to walk around in a little bubble. We are moving toward that.

> **Spell Check: The Good, the Bad, and the Ugly**
>
> If you take a writing assessment on a computer, you will probably have access to spell check. (That's good!) However, don't assume that the computer will catch all of your errors. (That's bad!) Spell check will not fined words witch are miss used butt spelled rite. (Ugly!)

> **Collaboration on Editing**
>
> Use the following to evaluate a partner's paragraph:
>
> - Are all spelling errors corrected?
> - Was a sentence fragment corrected?
> - Are verb tenses consistent throughout the paragraph?
>
> Identify specific errors that should be corrected. Revise your paragraphs on the basis of your partner's and your own evaluation.

Chapter 2

Writing an Argumentative Essay

The focus of an argumentative essay is to present a point of view on a topic using relevant reasons and strong evidence. Argumentative writing is different from persuasive writing in that the focus is on supporting a point of view with logical reasons, not emotional appeals. Also as the argument is developed, other points of view on the topic are explained and refuted.

LESSON 1 CLAIMS

Every argumentative essay begins with a claim. A **claim** is your point of view, or the main point you want readers to accept. It is more than just an opinion or a personal preference. It is a precise statement that

- is based upon a topic you have researched
- can be supported with accurate and reasonable information
- is arguable

Here's an example of significant, arguable, specific claim: "The United States should curtail illegal immigration from Mexico by building a fence along the border." Some people will agree; some will disagree and respond with evidence that supports their position. It's even possible that some may agree with curtailing illegal immigration, but disagree that a fence is the best solution.

The claim in an argumentative essay almost always appears in the first paragraph. Often it is the last sentence of the paragraph.

Types of Claims

Most claims serve one of the following purposes:

- clarify a definition
- explain a cause or effect
- make a judgment
- advocate an action

Activity 1A Identifying Claims

Underline the claim in this paragraph. On the lines below, explain why you selected it.

> Copyright law is intended to protect the right of authors, artists, and inventors to profit from their creations. When American copyright laws were first formulated in the 19th century, creativity was tied to physical objects. In the 21st century, creative works can be ephemeral. Music, for example, is no longer bound to physical objects such as vinyl albums or compact discs—it can also exist in digital form. Copyright and intellectual property laws formulated in a bygone time need to be modified to reflect the technological world in which we live. Artists still want to profit from their creations, but many people insist that music should be freely traded.

_____

_____

_____

Activity 1B Making Claims Specific

The more specific a claim is, the more effectively it can be argued. Of the three claims listed, label the one that is most specific as "good." Revise the other two claims to make them more specific.

Claim	Revision
1. The cost of getting a college education is too high.	
2. Drivers whose vehicles average less than 25 miles per gallon should pay a $50 per year surcharge on their license fees.	
3. Obesity is a problem in America.	

Activity 1C Identifying Strong Claims

In each row below, compare the statements in the first and second columns. Then explain why the statement in the Better Claim column is more effective as a claim for an argumentative essay.

Weak Claim	Better Claim	Explanation
1. The popular show *Saturday Night Live* was first broadcast on NBC in October 1975.	*Saturday Night Live* has become a powerful force in American culture since its premiere in 1975.	
2. Times have changed since the 1970s.	The changes in American life since 1975 are reflected in the content of each week's *Saturday Night Live*.	
3. *Saturday Night Live* satirizes current events and trends in American culture.	*Saturday Night Live* keeps Americans informed about current events by satirizing politics and pop culture.	

Activity 1D Writing a Claim

Below is an excerpt from a government press release on a program designed to eliminate alcohol-related traffic crashes. Read the passage and write a claim you can support using the information in the passage. ("BAC" stands for "blood alcohol content.")

Proof for a Claim

As you formulate a claim based on this passage, identify specific evidence in the text that could be used to support it.

Each year in the United States, nearly 10,000 people are killed in crashes involving alcohol-impaired drivers and more than 173,000 are injured, with 27,000 suffering incapacitating injuries. Since the mid-1990s, even as total highway fatalities have fallen, the proportion of deaths from accidents involving an alcohol-impaired driver has remained constant at around 30 percent. In the last 30 years, nearly 440,000 people have died in alcohol-related crashes.

Today, investigators cite research that showed that although impairment begins with the first drink, by 0.05 BAC, most drivers experience a decline in both cognitive and visual functions, which significantly increases the risk of a serious crash. Currently, over 100 countries on six continents have BAC limits set at 0.05 or lower. The NTSB has asked all 50 states to do the same. (Currently all states define driving with BAC at or above 0.08 percent as a crime.)

"The research clearly shows that drivers with a BAC above 0.05 are impaired and at a significantly greater risk of being involved in a crash where someone is killed or injured," said Deborah Hersman, chairwoman of the National Transportation Safety Board.

Source: "NTSB Unveils Interventions to Reach Zero Alcohol Impaired Crashes," National Transportation Safety Board Office of Public Affairs. *ntsb.gov*. May 14, 2013. Web. 31 January 2014.

_____

_____

_____

_____

_____

_____

Feedback on a Claim

To ensure that your claim is based upon an opinion, ask a friend to read your claim and tell you whether people might disagree with it.

LESSON 2 SUPPORT FOR CLAIMS

To convince your readers of your point of view, your claim requires the strongest possible support. Most support is one of two kinds:

- **Evidence** includes facts and informed judgments.
- **Reasons** include logical conclusions from evidence or ideas.

> ### Strength of Support
>
> Support is strong if it comes from a reliable source and is stated precisely. In general, more recent information is stronger than older information.

Activity 2A Identifying Strong Support

Imagine that you are writing a business proposal for your boss, the owner of a sandwich shop, arguing that there's sufficient business potential to open a second location. Each box includes a pair of similar sentences that might be used in the proposal. In the Explanation box, tell which sentence provides stronger support for your claim than the other one, and explain why.

A. Our downtown location is highly profitable, so we could afford to open a second location.	B. Our downtown location's monthly profit of $22,000 is more than enough to justify opening a second location.

1. Explanation

C. I think students attending the new high school would patronize a restaurant if they could.	D. A survey of students attending the new high school shows that 70 percent of them would patronize a conveniently-located restaurant.

2. Explanation

E. Youth unemployment rates in our town are high, so there's a pool of willing workers for us to draw from.	F. Youth unemployment rates in our town are high, and kids need things to do.

3. Explanation

Activity 2B Identifying Support for Claims

Read the following passage and follow the directions below it.

Hybrid Cars and Fuel Savings

One popular hybrid car model carries a 2013 list price of $26,950. The same model with a conventional gasoline engine lists for $23,490, a difference of $3,460. Based on normal driving patterns, the hybrid owner could expect to save about $500 a year on gasoline. So it would take about seven years of ownership before the hybrid owner made back the difference in the price she paid for the car.

Source: FuelEconomy.gov. U.S. Environmental Protection Agency, Office of Transportation and Air Quality

Multiple Claims

One fact can support alternate or even opposing claims. For example, figures showing the difference in price between a hybrid and a conventional engine car could be used to support either a claim that hybrids are too expensive or a claim that the price difference between a hybrid and a conventional engine car is insignificant. Similarly, data on the number of years it would take to make back the price difference could be used to argue either for or against a hybrid purchase, depending on whether you think it's reasonable to keep a car for more than seven years, or you prefer to get a new car more often.

1. Underline a phrase or sentence in the text that supports this claim:

   "Buying a hybrid car is too expensive for many drivers."

2. Underline a phrase or sentence in the text that supports this claim:

   "Fuel savings will easily cover the extra cost of a hybrid car."

LESSON 3 COUNTERCLAIMS

A point of view that disagrees with your claim is a **counterclaim**. If your claim is truly arguable, there will be other opinions or positions that contradict it. For example, consider the claim in Lesson 2 that the owner of a sandwich shop should open a second location near the new high school in your town. Possible counterclaims could include the following:

- It would be better to invest in a sandwich truck that could serve the high school along with other businesses around the city.

- An ice-cream shop would be more profitable than a sandwich shop.

Don't avoid writing about the opposing side of an argument. Including counterclaims and then refuting them will strengthen your position. Readers will view you as unbiased and knowledgable.

Activity 3A *Writing Counterclaims*

For each claim listed below, write a counterclaim.

Claim	Counterclaim
1. Higher average temperatures and more frequent violent storms represent natural climatic fluctuations.	
2. Paying college coaches astronomically high salaries sends the message that sports are more important than academics.	
3. No one has the right to read someone else's e-mail messages.	

Activity 3B *Responding to Counterclaims*

In the following paragraph, place parentheses around the claim. Underline the counterclaim and the evidence supporting it. Circle the response to the evidence supporting the counterclaim.

Trade professions, such as machinists, electricians, plumbers, and building contractors, are often better options for high school graduates than entering a job that requires a college education. Some argue that a college education is necessary for life in the 21st century, and it is true that nearly two-thirds of all jobs require a college degree. However, there's currently a shortage of workers in the skilled trades. Thus, a person trained in one of these professions has an excellent opportunity to earn a good income while performing a vital service.

LESSON 4 EVIDENCE FROM SOURCES

Argumentative writing is always based on information from reading sources. In some testing situations, you may be provided with several texts on the same topic. To prepare you to write an essay, the test may first ask you to answer some questions on the sources. Tasks may include defining key vocabulary terms, identifying main ideas, and writing a summary.

The following set of activities asks questions about a source that provides evidence you could use to write an essay arguing for or against the practice of marketing prescription drugs directly to consumers.

Activity 4A Understanding Vocabulary

Read the following text and answer the vocabulary questions that follow it.

> ### Source 1
>
> ### Prescription Drug Advertising: A Healthy Choice for Americans
> *excerpted from an article that appeared in a medical magazine*
>
> A decade ago, a study by the Henry J. Kaiser Family Foundation found that the pharmaceutical industry makes over four dollars for every dollar spent on direct advertising of prescription drugs to American consumers. Although this is often invoked as a reason why this advertising is a bad thing, in actual fact, the profitability of the pharmaceutical industry, thanks in part to this advertising, has major benefits for American consumers.
>
> Developing new drugs is expensive. *Forbes* magazine recently reported that the cost of research, development, testing, approval by the Food and Drug Administration, manufacturing, and marketing to get just one new drug to market can exceed 5 billion dollars.
>
> Where does this money come from?
>
> Pharmaceutical companies can't print money; they aren't owned by infinitely wealthy people with money to burn. They need to turn a profit to stay in business, and advertising helps.

Reading to Argue

Before writing a claim or forming a position on a topic, you should conduct thorough research. After reading about an issue in depth, you can decide on the position you want to argue for. After examining all the facts and evidence, you may find that your original position has changed. Plus, an informed reader writes a stronger paper.

Connecting Sections of Text

In the first paragraph, the phrase "in actual fact" is used to set up a contrast between the idea that advertising is a bad thing and the idea that profitability resulting from advertising is a benefit to the consumer. Adverbs and adverbial phrases such as *also*, *furthermore*, *moreover*, and *more importantly* signal that the writer is presenting additional support for the claim. For more on words that connect ideas, see Chapter 1, page 9.

continued on next page

continued from previous page

Furthermore, the more profitable a pharmaceutical company is, the more money it will have to put back into research, to discover new drugs and refine existing ones. Without these profits, pharmaceutical companies would find it more difficult to develop the drugs that have lengthened, or saved, the lives of millions of Americans.

When patients know what prescription drugs can do, they become partners with their physicians in making their healthcare decisions. Prescription drug advertising provides consumers with information pre-viously known only to physicians. A well-informed consumer is a better consumer, and in the case of prescription drugs, a healthier one.

Adapted from forbes.com and procon.org

Part A

Circle the letter before the choice that best explains the key idea in "Prescription Drug Advertising a Healthy Practice for Americans."

    a. The profitability of pharmaceutical advertising is sometimes criticized as a bad thing.

    b. The Food and Drug Administration must approve all new drugs before they can be sold to the public.

    c. Increased funding for research is one of the most significant benefits of prescription drug advertising.

    d. The benefits of prescription drug advertising flow to American consumers in a variety of ways.

> **Key Idea**
>
> The first of a pair of questions might ask you to identify the key idea in a text. A second question might ask you to identify one or more statements that provide evidence for your choice.

Part B

Circle the letter before two pieces of evidence from "Prescription Drug Advertising a Healthy Practice for Americans" that support the key idea you identified in Part A.

    a. "The pharmaceutical industry makes over four dollars for every dollar spent on direct advertising. . . ."

    b. "Developing new drugs is expensive."

    c. "Without these profits . . . companies would find it more difficult to develop the drugs that have [saved] millions of Americans."

    d. "When patients know what prescription drugs can do, they become partners with their physicians in making their healthcare decisions."

Source 2

Selling Sickness: How Drug Ads Changed Health Care

The Nielsen Co. estimates that there's an average of 80 drug ads every hour of every day on American television. And those ads clearly produce results:

"Something like a third of consumers who've seen a drug ad have talked to their doctor about it," says Julie Donohue, a professor of public health at the University of Pittsburgh who is considered a leading expert on this subject.

"About two-thirds of those have asked for a prescription. And the majority of people who ask for a prescription have that request honored."

Whether the increase in the number of prescription drugs taken is good or bad for patient health is an open question. There's evidence on both sides. What's not up for debate is this: By taking their case to patients instead of doctors, drug companies increased the amount of money we spend on medicine in America.

Source: Spiegel, Alix. "Selling Sickness: How Drug Ads Changed Health Care." October 13, 2009. *npr.org.* Web. 12 February 2014.

Activity 4B Writing a Summary

Write a summary of "Selling Sickness: How Drug Ads Changed Health Care."

_____

_____

_____

_____

_____

_____

Collaborating on Summaries

A summary is a shorter version of a text. In a summary, include the key idea and the most important support for it. You should leave out most details.

After you write your summary for this activity, share it with another student through e-mail or a social media site and ask him or her to evaluate it.

LESSON 5

HOW TO WRITE AN ARGUMENTATIVE ESSAY

Below are more sources about the direct advertising of prescription drugs to consumers. Following it is a model demonstrating the five steps in writing an argumentative essay. Use these five steps to help you write your own essays.

Using Multiple Sources

When writing an argumentative essay for a test, you might be asked to read additional sources about the same topic as a source you have already read and answered questions about. These additional sources will provide more evidence to use in your essay.

Source 3

Arguments Opposing Direct-to-Consumer Ads

Leads to inappropriate prescribing. If a patient's request for an advertised drug is clinically inappropriate and the health care provider is unable or unwilling to correct the patient's perception that it is a good choice, this situation may lead to unnecessary or harmful prescribing. An additional problem mentioned by critics is that patients may withhold information to fit a particular profile that they saw in DTC ads in an attempt to get the doctor to prescribe a drug they want but that might not be appropriate for them.

Data regarding whether DTCPA (direct-to-consumer pharmaceutical advertising) leads to inappropriate prescribing have been mixed. Although studies have shown that only 2% to 7% of drug requests by patients are successful, one study reported that such requests were made during about 40% of doctor visits and were successful more than half the time. Furthermore, more than half of the physicians in this study said that they prescribed the drug in order to accommodate the patient's request. Similarly, 94% of ONPs (oncology nurse practitioners) reported having had a patient request for an advertised drug, and 40% said they experienced one to five requests per week. Alarmingly, 74% of the ONPs said patients asked for an inappropriate drug, which 43% said they sometimes felt pressured to prescribe. . . .

In a national survey, 39% of physicians and 30% of patients felt that DTCPA interfered with the physician–patient relationship.

Ventola, C. Lee. "Direct-to-Consumer Pharmaceutical Advertising: Therapeutic or Toxic?. *ncbi. nlm.nih.gov.* U.S. National Library of Medicine-National Institutes of Health. 2011. Web. 24 Jan. 2014.

Web Site Reliability

Many Web sites include an "About" tab that provides background on the person or organization that produces the site. This information can help you evaluate the reliability of information on the site.

Source 4

According to Yahoo! Finance's industry summary, the average profit margin for generic drug companies as of April 2013 is 5.4 percent. The largest average profit margin is for major drug manufacturers at 18.4 percent. This group includes Pfizer, AstraZeneca and Bristol-Myers Squibb.

Source: Wright, Tiffany. "The Average Profit Margin Of Pharmaceuticals." *azcentral.com.* Web. 10 February 2014.

Step 1. Understand the prompt.

The directions for writing an essay are called the **prompt.** The verbs in it tell you what to do. Here is an example of a prompt:

> You have read two texts commenting on direct advertising of prescription drugs to consumers. Take a position on this issue. You might favor drug advertising or be opposed to it, or you might choose to express a different opinion. Use textual evidence from the sources to support your claim.

Activity 5A Analyzing the Prompt

In the prompt above, underline key words and phrases that tell you what to do. Then, rewrite the prompt in your own words below.

_____

_____

_____

_____

_____

_____

Step 2. Take notes on the sources.

You may have already analyzed the sources, but now you should take notes on them with the prompt in mind. Look for specific facts and ideas that you can use in your essay. It is often helpful to organize your ideas using a graphic organizer, such as a chart or a Venn diagram.

Evaluate your notes by identifying the strongest and most relevant evidence for both your claim and your counterclaim. Also consider which evidence will be the most relevant to your audience. Teenagers have different levels of knowledge and values than adults. Decide which reasons and evidence will be most likely to convince your readers.

> **Collaborate About Prompts**
>
> After you write your prompt, trade it with a partner. Discuss any differences in how you interpreted the prompt.

Activity 5B Analyzing Sources

The chart below includes notes from the two sources about prescription drug advertising shown on previous pages. Fill in the empty cells with notes from the sources.

Support for Advertising	Against Advertising
Drug company profits fund further research and development. ("Profitable")	Patients may push to take drugs they don't need.
Claim:	
Counterclaim:	

Step 3. Organize your ideas.

Use an outline to organize the ideas for your essay. Like most texts, an argumentative essay should include an introduction, body, and conclusion.

> **Strong Opening**
>
> The first lines of the introduction should catch the attention of readers. Try using a powerful anecdote, a compelling statistic, or maybe just a clever turn of phrase. The goal is to engage the reader and make him or her want to keep reading.

The **introduction** is the first paragraph of an essay. It should identify the topic and state the claim.

The **body** is the main part of an essay. It should present the support for the claim—both reasons and evidence. In addition, it should present at least one counterclaim and a response to it. On the next page are three options for organizing the body of the essay.

As you develop your outline, keep in mind the importance of presenting your reasons logically. Use transitional words and phrases (*first, next, in support of, on the other hand*) to help the reader distinguish among your claims, reasons, evidence, and counterclaims. The following chart offers some options for organizing an argumentative essay.

Option 1	Option 2	Option 3
Reason 1 with evidence	Counterclaim with rebuttal	Reason 1 with evidence
Reason 2 with evidence	Reason 1 with evidence	Counterclaim related to reason 1 with rebuttal
Reason 3 with evidence	Reason 2 with evidence	Reason 2 with evidence
Counterclaim with rebuttal	Reason 3 with evidence	Counterclaim related to reason 2 with rebuttal
Strengths: support flows smoothly from the statement of the claim in the first paragraph	**Strengths:** allows writer to address readers' views immediately in situations where most readers agree with the counterclaim	Reason 3 with evidence
		Counterclaim related to reason 3 with rebuttal
		Strengths: excellent for long essays that include many counterclaims

The **conclusion** is the last paragraph of an essay. It should either summarize the main support for the claim or state the strongest support for the claim. It should always restate the claim.

Activity 5C Analyzing an Outline

On the following page is an outline that a student might have written before drafting an argumentative essay about prescription drug advertising. As you read it, mark it as follows:

1. Circle the heading for each of the three main parts of the outline.

2. Underline the two places where the claim is specifically mentioned.

3. Put a check mark next to the counterclaim the writer will address.

Strong Ending

Often, the last line of the conclusion is a short or dramatic sentence that will stick in the minds of readers.

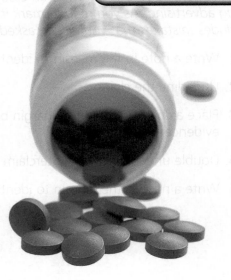

Sample Outline: Direct Advertising of Prescription Drugs

Claim: Direct advertising of prescription drugs should not be legal in the United States.

I.   Introduction
    A. Our health is the most important possession we own.
    B. Direct advertising of prescription drugs is hazardous to the health of Americans.

II.   Body
    A. Advertising causes consumers to self-diagnose instead of trusting their doctors, resulting in bad health decisions.
    B. Counterclaim: Drug companies claim that profits are used for research and develop better drugs, but they are also making a huge profit.
    C. Drug advertising is driving up health care costs for everyone.

III. Conclusion
    A. Direct-to-consumer drug advertising is an unwise practice and should be ended.
    B. Americans are more medicated and poorer as a result.

Step 4. Write the draft.

Using your notes and your outline, write your essay.

Activity 5D Analyzing Organization

On the next page is the draft of an essay about direct-to-consumer drug advertising. As you read it, mark it as indicated below. The draft includes mistakes that you will be asked to correct in the next activity.

1. Write a note in the margin to identify the introduction.

2. Underline the claim.

3. Place a check mark in the margin beside three specific pieces of evidence from the sources.

4. Double underline the counterclaim.

5. Write a note in the margin to identify the conclusion.

Spell-Check

If you write your essay on a computer, spell-check will highlight many errors. However, it may not catch a mistake if the mistake is also a correctly spelled word. Imagine you meant to write "It's over here, then." Instead, you typed "Its over hear, than." Spell-check might miss all three errors in the sentence.

Sample Draft: Direct Advertising of Prescription Drugs

One of my great-grandmother's favorite sayings was, "You don't have anything if you don't have your health." She lived to be 101 years old was never sick in her life until the week she died. She was living proof that our health is the most important possession we have. I believe that the multibillion dollar business of advertising prescription drugs directly to American consumers is a threat to our health, and it's something that should be stopped.

First, advertising gives consumers a false sense that they can accurately diagnose their own health issues. Advertising has a strong impact but can't present all of the information needed in a thirty-second ad. Consumers self-diagnose, then march into their doctor's office and ask for medicine. In one study, 74% of nurse practitioners said patients asked for an inappropriate drug, and 43% said they sometimes felt pressured to prescribe the drug (Ventola). This puts a strain on the relationship between doctors and patients. Patients mistrust their doctors; doctors feel their authority is being questioned. Almost 40% of physicians felt that drug ads interfered with the physician-patient relationship (Ventola).

Drug companies claim that the money they make from advertising goes into researching and producing new drugs that will continue to help the consumer stay healthy. Granted, the cost of producing a new drug is high; some estimate the cost at over $5 million (*Forbes*). However, drug companies are still making a profit. Some of the bigger companies like Pfizer, AstraZeneca and Bristol-Myers Squibb made a profit of 18 percent in the first quarter of 2013 (Wright). Clearly not all money is flowing back into research and development.

Drug advertising is driving up the cost of health care in America. Julie Donohue, a professor of public health at the University of Pittsburgh says that about two-thirds of people who see a drug commercial "have asked for a prescription. And the majority of people who

> ### Citations
>
> This essay uses intext citations to identify sources of evidence. For lessons citing sources, see Chapter 4, Lesson 4, "Citations and Quotations," pages 57–58.

continued on next page

continued from previous page

ask for a prescription have that request honored" (Spiegel). More drugs being prescribed means more insurance claims, which results in higher rates. And new drugs cost more than ones that have been on the market a while. In the end, the consumer pays the price and the drug companies earn bigger and bigger profits.

Simply put, direct-to-consumer drug advertising is hurting the health of Americans. Instead of trusting health care professionals, consumers demand the latest drugs. Americans are not healthier, just poorer and over medicated.

Step 5. Revise your essay.

After you write a draft, read it again carefully. Make changes to improve it. For example, you might rearrange ideas so they flow more smoothly or add content to make your argument stronger.

Argumentative essays should be written in formal style. The ideas should be based upon research instead of personal experiences. Personal anecdotes have emotional appeal but argumentative writing should appeal mainly to logic using reasons and evidence. To make your argument as strong as possible, use a third-person viewpoint, objectively stating what you or other people believe. This means you should

- not use first-person pronouns, such as *I, me, we,* or *our*

- not use second-person pronouns, such as *you*

Online Peer Revision

Post your argumentative essay online, share it with a classmate, and ask them to evaluate your arguments. Have them use the comments feature to give positive feedback and make suggestions.

Activity 5E *Maintaining Point of View*

The following is the introduction from the student model. Underline every time a first- or second-person pronoun is used.

One of my great-grandmother's favorite sayings was, "You don't have anything if you don't have your health." She lived to be 101 years old was never sick in her life until the week she died. She was living proof that our health is the most important possession we have. I believe that the multibillion dollar business of advertising prescription drugs directly to American consumers is a threat to our health, and it's something that should be stopped.

Use the following questions to evaluate the paragraph—either on your own or with a partner.

1. Is the story about the writer's grandmother interesting or too informal? Will the audience find the great-grandmother's quote convincing or just one person's opinion?

2. What interesting facts or statistics could be pulled from the sources and used in the introduction?

3. Does using the phrase "I believe" add strength to the claim or would the claim be stronger if it were omitted?

Based upon your answers to the questions above, rewrite the introduction on the lines below.

_____

_____

_____

_____

_____

_____

> ### Collaboration on Introduction Revision
>
> Ask a partner to check your revised introduction. It should be interesting, have a formal tone, and include a strong, clear claim.

Step 6. Edit and proofread your essay.

Follow the norms and conventions regarding spelling, punctuation, grammar, and usage. Fix any errors you find and consider changes to make your text flow more smoothly.

Check to make sure you use hyphens correctly. Use a hyphen

- to join two or more words serving a single adjective before a noun.

    a well-known athlete
    a one-way street

    However, compound modifiers after a noun are not hyphenated.

    The athlete was well known.
    The technology was out of date.

- with compound numbers.

    forty-six   ninety-nine

- with the prefixes *ex-, self-, all-,* and *-elect*; and between a prefix and a capitalized word; and with figures or letters.

ex-husband	mid-September	T-shirt
pre-Civil War	mid-1980s	anti-American

Activity 5F Using Hyphens

Cross out the words containing hyphen mistakes and then write them correctly on the line.

1. Pre 1983, no drug ads were shown on television.

_____

2. In 2008, drug companies poured over fifty seven billion dollars into marketing. Up to date figures may be even higher.

_____

Activity 5G Proofreading

The paragraph below contains at least 12 errors in spelling, punctuation, grammar, and usage. Underline the error and then rewrite the paragraph, correcting all of the errors.

In 1999, the Food and Drug administration issued a document called "Guidance for Industry: Consumer-Directed Broadcast Advertisements;" which was intended to help drug companies taylor their advertising to serve what the f.d.a. considered to be the public interest. The ads required to be neither false nor misleading they were to present a balance between information about effectiveness and information about risk, includeing a thorough statement of all of the products most important risk information. All information in the ads was presented in consumer-friendly langauge. One especially important provision, required the ads to mention that the products are available only by prescription. That only a health care professional can decide whether the product is appropriate for the patient.

_____

_____

_____

_____

_____

_____

_____

_____

Hyphens and Meaning

Always consider your intended meaning when hyphenating compound modifiers before a noun. Consider the following:

• Under the seat I found a hot water bottle.

• Put a hot-water bottle on your sore muscle.

Placing a hyphen in the phrase hot-water indicates that the two words are working together to modify the word *water*.

LESSON 6 YOU TRY IT

Now it is your turn to write an argumentative essay. Use what you have learned in this chapter about claims, counterclaims, and evidence. Follow the steps outlined in the last lesson. They are also listed in the box on the right.

Steps in Writing an Argumentative Essay

1. Understand the prompt.
2. Take notes on the sources.
3. Organize your ideas.
4. Write the draft.
5. Revise your essay.
6. Edit and proofread your essay.

Activity 6A *Writing an Argumentative Essay*

Write an argumentative essay in response to one of the following prompts. Use information from at least three sources.

A. Academics vs. Sports	B. Official English
High school sports have a dominant place in American culture. At the same time students are falling behind the world academically. Is the emphasis on sports having a negative effect on high school students? Take a position on this question. Write an argumentative essay in support of your claim. Address at least one counterclaim and support your ideas with relevant evidence from your research.	For many years, efforts have been made to declare English the official language of the United States. Conduct research on the official-English movement, then write an argumentative essay taking a position on whether English should be legally declared the country's official language. Support your with reasons and evidence. Address at least one counterclaim in your essay.

Checklist

Use the following checklist to edit and revise your essay.

My writing has . . .	
DEVELOPMENT	❏ a clear central claim ❏ strong supporting evidence ❏ one or more counterclaims
ORGANIZATION	❏ a clear introduction, body, and conclusion ❏ good transitions ❏ logical order
EVIDENCE	❏ strong, relevant textual evidence ❏ enough evidence to be convincing
LANGUAGE & STYLE	❏ precise, appropriate word choice ❏ a formal, objective tone
GRAMMAR, SPELLING, & PUNCTUATION	❏ standard grammar ❏ correct spelling ❏ proper punctuation

Writing an Informative Essay

The purpose of an informative/explanatory essay is to explain or to provide information about a topic. When you explain how a bill becomes a law, describe the steps you used in a science experiment, or analyze three causes of the Civil War, you are using informative writing.

LESSON 1 THESIS STATEMENT

The purpose of your informative essay should be communicated in the main idea statement, also called the thesis statement. A **thesis statement** should clearly state the central idea of an essay. It should

- be clear and precise
- fulfill the requirements of the test prompt
- be based upon the texts you were asked to read

A good thesis statement should not begin with "My main idea is . . ." or "In this essay I will. . . ."

> **Informative Essays**
> ....
> - Increase the reader's knowledge of a subject
> - Help the reader understand a process or procedure

Activity 1A Making a Thesis Statement Precise

Select the statement below that is most precise and label it "good."
Rewrite the other two to make them more precise.

Thesis Statement	Revision
1. This paper is about the steps you have to take to find out what is wrong with a computer.	
2. A number of different search engines are available.	
3. President Obama's first inaugural address echoed themes from the speeches of Abraham Lincoln.	

Activity 1B Writing a Thesis Statement

Below is an excerpt from a government report on trash. Read the facts and then write a strong thesis statement.

Municipal Solid Waste

Municipal Solid Waste (MSW)—more commonly known as trash or garbage—consists of everyday items we use and then throw away, such as product packaging, grass clippings, furniture, clothing, bottles, food scraps, newspapers, appliances, paint, and batteries.

- In 1960 the United States generated 88 million tons of municipal solid waste (MSW); almost 83 million tons were disposed of in landfills. Just over 6 percent was recycled.

- MSW generation continued to increase until 2007, when it was 257 million tons; 140 million tons went to landfills, and about 31 percent was recycled. After 2007 the rate of generation began to decrease.

- In 2011 the United States generated 250 million tons of MSW; 134 million tons went to landfills, and over 34 percent was recycled.

Source: Environmental Protection Agency.

Thesis Statement:

_____

_____

_____

_____

LESSON 2 SUPPORT FOR THE THESIS STATEMENT

Your thesis statement should be developed with appropriate supporting details. These might include facts, examples, incidents, analogies, or causes and effects. Strong supporting details are relevant, or directly related, to the thesis statement.

> **Maintaining Purpose**
>
> When choosing supporting details, remember the focus of informative writing is to convey ideas, not to persuade the reader to agree with your opinion.

Activity 2A Evaluating Supporting Details

Cross out sentences that would not be good supporting details for the thesis statement. In the margin, write notes explaining why.

Thesis Statement: Different people can see the same color in different ways.

Possible Supporting Details

- The human eye can distinguish millions of separate colors.
- Light receptors in the eye send messages to the brain, which translates what we see into color.
- Isaac Newton introduced the science of color in 1666.
- Some insects can see ultraviolet colors invisible to the human eye.
- In some people the ability to see color is impaired; they still see color, but some colors are transmitted to the brain differently.
- Most people with color impairment don't realize that objects they see as having the same color look different to other people.
- In visual arts, color theory is a way to organize what we know about colors.
- People with a condition called synesthesia may see colors when they hear sounds.

Activity 2B Writing Supporting Details

Write three good details you might use to support this thesis statement: America's television viewing habits have changed over the last few years.

1. _____

_____

2. _____

_____

3. _____

_____

LESSON 3 ANALYZING SOURCES

A test that asks you to write an informative essay may first ask you to read and answer questions about a passage or passages that you will use when writing your essay. If you are asked to write a summary of a text, include the main idea and a few key supporting points.

Activity 3A Writing a Summary

Read the following text and underline key ideas.

Source 1

Employment Projections: 2012–2022

Occupations and industries related to healthcare are projected to add the most new jobs between 2012 and 2022. Total employment is projected to increase 10.8 percent, or 15.6 million, during the decade. Most of the 10.8 percent employment growth is projected to be in service-providing industries.

The health care and social assistance sector is projected to grow at an annual rate of 2.6 percent, adding 5 million jobs between 2012 and 2022. This accounts for nearly one-third of the total projected increase in jobs. The growth reflects, in part, the demand for healthcare workers to address the needs of an aging population.

Five industry sectors are projected to have decreases in employment: manufacturing (-549,500); federal government (-407,500); agriculture, forestry, fishing, and hunting (-223,500); information (-65,200); and utilities (-56,400).

Occupation Employment

Four major occupational groups are projected to grow more than 20 percent—nearly double the overall growth—from 2012 to 2022: health-care support occupations (28.1 percent), healthcare practitioners and technical occupations (21.5 percent), construction and extraction occupations (21.4 percent), and personal care and service occupations (20.9 percent).

Education and Training

Occupations typically requiring postsecondary education for entry generally had higher median wages ($57,770) in 2012 and are projected to grow faster (14.0 percent) between 2012 and 2022 than occupations that typically require a high school diploma or less ($27,670 and 9.1 percent).

Occupations that do not typically require postsecondary education are projected to add 8.8 million jobs between 2012 and 2022, accounting for more than half of all new jobs. These occupations employed nearly two-thirds of workers in 2012.

Source: United States Department of Labor. Bureau of Labor Statistics.

Write a summary of Source 1 from page 37.

_____

_____

_____

_____

_____

_____

_____

 ## Activity 3B Answering Questions About a Source

Read the following text and answer the questions that follow.

Source 2

Metal and Plastic Machine Workers

Metal and plastic machine workers set up and operate machines that cut, shape, and form metal and plastic materials or pieces. Metal and plastic machine workers are employed mainly in factories. A few months of on-the-job training are enough for most workers to learn basic machine operations. Although not always required, employers prefer to hire workers who have a high school diploma. The median hourly wage for metal and plastic machine workers was $15.84 in May 2012.

Employment of metal and plastic machine workers is projected to decline 6 percent from 2012 to 2022. Employment will decline due to advances in technology, foreign competition, and changing demand for the goods these workers produce.

Licensed Practical and Licensed Vocational Nurses

Licensed practical nurses (LPNs) and licensed vocational nurses (LVNs) provide basic nursing care. They work in nursing homes and extended care facilities, hospitals, physicians' offices, and private homes. LPNs and LVNs must complete a state-approved educational program, which typically takes about 1 year to complete. They must also be licensed. The median hourly wage for LPNs and LVNs was $19.97 in May 2012.

continued on next page

continued from previous page

Duties of LPNs and LVNs vary. They may reinforce teaching done by registered nurses regarding how family members should care for a relative; help to deliver, care for, and feed infants; collect samples for testing and do routine laboratory tests; or feed patients who need help eating.

Employment of LPNs and LVNs is projected to grow 25 percent from 2012 to 2022, much faster than the average for all occupations. As the baby-boom population ages, the overall need for healthcare services is expected to increase.

Source: United States Department of Labor. Bureau of Labor Statistics.

Part A

Which of the following sentences best summarizes the main idea of the passage?

a. Different occupations call for different training and skills.

b. Machinists work in factories, while nurses work in hospitals and nursing homes.

c. The work done by licensed practical nurses and licensed vocational nurses varies.

d. The demand for machine workers will decline, but the need for nurses will increase.

Part B

Choose two of the following sentences that could be used to support your answer to Part A.

a. A few months of on-the-job training are enough for most workers to learn basic machine operations.

b. LPNs and LVNs must complete a state-approved educational program, which typically takes about 1 year to complete.

c. Employment of metal and plastic machine workers is projected to decline 6 percent from 2012 to 2022.

d. Duties of LPNs and LVNs vary.

e. Employment of LPNs and LVNs is projected to grow 25 percent from 2012 to 2022 . . .

LESSON 4 HOW TO WRITE AN INFORMATIVE ESSAY

The following steps demonstrate the process of writing an informative essay.

Step 1. Understand the prompt.

The directions for writing an essay are called the **prompt.** The verbs in the prompt tell you what to do. Here is an example of a prompt:

> The U.S. economy once relied on producing goods, but today's economy is largely service-based. Write an essay explaining how this change will affect U.S. jobs and workers in the future.

Activity 4A Analyzing the Prompt

In the prompt above, underline key words that tell you what to do. Write a purpose statement for your essay below.

My purpose is to: _____

_____

Step 2. Take notes on the sources.

You have already analyzed the sources, but now you should take notes on them with the prompt in mind. Go back to the texts you read. Look for specific statements that will fit with the purpose of your essay.

Activity 4B Gathering Ideas

Fill in the organizer below with facts from the sources.

Change in U.S. economy from producing goods to offering services	
Facts About Jobs (Causes)	Impact on Workers (Effects)

Writing an Essay

Use the following steps to help you write an informative essay.

1. Understand the prompt.
2. Take notes on the sources.
3. Write a thesis statement.
4. Develop a complete outline.
5. Write the draft.
6. Revise your essay.
7. Edit and proofread your essay.

Step 3. Write a thesis statement.

Once you've gathered some ideas to include in your essay, write a thesis statement. Your thesis statement will be included in the introduction of your essay and will guide the ideas you write about in the body of your paper.

Activity 4C Writing a Thesis Statement

Based upon your notes, write a thesis statement for your paper.

_____

_____

_____

_____

Step 4. Develop a complete outline.

An informative essay should include an introduction, a body, and a conclusion.

The **introduction** should introduce the topic and include the thesis statement.

The **body** should develop the thesis statement using supporting details.

The **conclusion** should restate the thesis statement. It should give a sense of closure to the writing.

Activity 4D Analyzing an Outline

On the next page is an outline that a student might have written before drafting an informative essay about jobs in a changing economy. As you read it, mark it as follows:

1. Circle the heading for each of the three main parts of the outline.

2. Underline two places where the thesis statement is specifically mentioned.

3. Are the main points in the body in logical order? Why or why not?

_____

_____

_____

_____

Sample Outline: Skills for a Changing Economy

I. Introduction

   A. U.S. textile mills, auto plants, and other manufacturers were once major employers. Today, there are more jobs in service industries than in manufacturing.

   B. Thesis Statement: The changing face of U.S. industry requires workers to learn different skills.

II. Body

   A. Jobs in manufacturing are in decline, while service industry jobs are increasing.

   B. Manufacturing jobs often required no academic qualifications and provided on-the-job training.

   C. Some service jobs require postsecondary education.

III. Conclusion

   A. Service industry jobs can offer more varied work and higher wages than manufacturing jobs.

   B. In a changing economy, workers must learn the skills needed for jobs in expanding sectors.

Step 6. Write the draft.

Using your notes and your outline, write your essay. When writing a first draft, write fairly quickly. Focus on getting your ideas down. Later there will be time to evaluate content and organization.

Activity 4E Analyzing a Draft

On the next page is a draft of an essay based on the prompt given. The draft contains some errors which you will be correcting in a later activity. As you read it, mark it as follows.

1. Write a note in the margin to identify the introduction and the conclusion.

2. Underline the thesis statement.

3. Place a check in the margin beside three specific pieces of evidence from the sources.

4. Circle three transitional phrases.

Sample Draft: Skills for a Changing Economy

Industry and employment change over time. U.S. textile mills, auto plants, and other manufacturers were once major employers. Today, there are more jobs in service industries than in manufacturing. The changing face of U.S. industry requires workers to learn different skills in order to remain employed.

The Changing Job Market

Some 15.6 million new jobs will be added to the U.S. economy between 2012 and 2022 according to the Bureau of Labor Statistics. Many industries will see job growth with some of the greatest increases being seen in the health care and social assistance sector. About 5 million of the 15.8 million new jobs that are being projected or almost one third of the total new jobs will be in the health care and social assistance sector. One sector that decreases will be seen in is manufacturing, where 500,000 will probably be lost in the same period (bls.org).

Different Job Skills

The overall increase in the number of jobs are good for the economy. However, the thousands of workers who lose manufacturing jobs won't simply be able to step into new jobs in health care. The skills, knowledge, and training required in the two sectors are too different. Many jobs in manafacturing do not require any academic qualifications or prior training. For example, becoming a metal and plastic machine worker does not always require a high school diploma, workers learn through on-the-job training (bls.org).

On the other hand, most health care sector jobs require some formal training after high school. The training to become a licensed practical nurse (LPN) or licensed vocational nurse (LVN) takes about a year. As the name implies, LPNs and LVNs must also be licensed to work.

continued on next page

Use of Headers

Notice that headers are used to introduce the content of each paragraph in the body. Headers can aid the reader's comprehension, especially when you are writing about complex ideas.

Citations

In some writing assignments, you will need to identify your sources in your text. For examples showing how to do this see Chapter 4, Lesson 4, "Citations and Quotations" on pages 57–58.

continued from previous page

Challenge and Reward

Although service industry jobs often require more formal training than manufacturing jobs, there are also benefits to this kind of work. The day-to-day tasks are often more varied, which helps keep the work interesting. There may also be a financal benefit in higher wages. For example, the median hourly wage in 2012 for metal and plastic machine workers was $15.84, while for LPNs and LVNs it was $19.97 (bls.org). Over time, the higher hourly wage would make up for the additional time spent training.

Of course, the biggest benefit of working in the health care and social assistance sector is simply that: working. Based on the Department of Labor's projections, there will be plenty of jobs available for those with the right training and skills.

Step 7. Revise your essay.

After you write a draft, read it carefully, watching for problems such as misplaced modifiers, inconsistent tone, and shifts in verb voice or mood. Consider how you would revise the following paragraph from the student model.

> Some 15.6 million new jobs will be added to the U.S. economy between 2012 and 2022 according to the Bureau of Labor Statistics. Many industries will see job growth with some of the greatest increases being seen in the health care and social assistance sector. About 5 million of the 15.8 million new jobs that are being projected or almost one third of the total new jobs will be in the health care and social assistance sector. One sector that decreases will be seen in is manufacturing, where half a million jobs will probably be lost in the same period.

Notice that the syntax, or the arrangement of words, in this paragraph shows little variety. The sentences are similar in length, structure, and order: ideas are added one after the other, with no focus or emphasis, no sense that one idea is more important than another. This lack of emphasis makes it difficult to understand the relationship between ideas.

Effective writers use all the tools at their disposal—syntax, punctuation, and word choice—to create interest and call attention to important

Vary Syntax for Effect

To add variety to your writing, focus on how you start sentences. If you usually begin with the subject, try opening with an adverb or abverbial phrase that modifies the verb in the sentence, such as *Happily* or *During science class*.

ideas. Sentences may be short or long; they can be simple, compound, complex, or even compound-complex. To add emphasis, try shifting the placement of phrases or clauses.

Analyze the sentences in the paragraph you just read on effective writing. Notice how the sentences vary in length and structure. Each one acts as an example of the technique it describes.

- The first sentence uses two dashes to add emphasis to information that is parenthetical, or not essential for understanding the sentence.

- The second sentence uses a semicolon to join two independent clauses, making a compound sentence.

- The last sentence begins with an infinitive phrase (*To add emphasis*).

Activity 4F Using Varied Syntax to Improve Clarity

On the lines below, rewrite the student model paragraph about the changing job market on page 44. Use a variety of sentence types and patterns to add focus and clarity.

_____

_____

_____

_____

_____

_____

_____

_____

_____

_____

_____

_____

_____

Analyzing a Text for Sentence Variety

Choose a novel or short story you are reading in class. Analyze one paragraph by recording the number of sentences that begin with a subject and verb, with a prepositional phrase, a subordinate clause, etc. Does the writer use good variety? Then analyze the same paragraph for sentence length. Does the writer use short and long sentences to speed up or slow down the pace of the writing? Think about how you can apply what you learned to your own writing.

Activity 4G Rereading an Essay

Read the draft and answer these questions about possible revisions:

Collaborate on Rereading Essays

In a small group, discuss the strengths and weaknesses of the draft essay. For example, identify where the draft uses relevant facts, concrete details, and precise language. Also identify where the draft needs revision.

1. Is the thesis statement clear and precise? Explain your answer.

_____

_____

2. Is the thesis statement supported with well-chosen facts? Are the facts sufficient? Are the terms explained clearly?

_____

_____

_____

_____

_____

3. Does the writing express a formal style and objective tone? Give examples to show whether the text is formal and objective.

_____

_____

_____

_____

4. Is the conclusion of the essay well developed? Rewrite the final paragraph so that the conclusion is stronger.

_____

_____

_____

_____

_____

_____

Step 8. Edit and proofread your essay.

After revising the content and style of your essay, read through it carefully for mistakes in grammar, spelling, and punctuation.

The following sentence from the model has a problem commonly found in student writing:

> For example, becoming a metal and plastic machine worker does not always require a high school diploma, workers learn through on-the-job training.

This is a run-on sentence. A **run-on sentence** is two or more sentences written together as one sentence. Run-ons can be corrected by

- creating two separate sentences
- using the words *and, but, or,* or another conjunction and a comma
- using a semicolon

Activity 4H Correcting Run-on Sentences

Using three different types of correction, rewrite the run-one sentence above. Then place a star by the one you think works best.

1. Two separate sentences

_____

_____

2. One compound sentence with a conjunction (*and, but,* or *or*) that fits the relationship between the two independent clauses

_____

_____

3. One compound sentence joined by a semicolon

_____

_____

Activity 4I Proofreading a Model Essay

Proofread the model essay by finding and correcting the following errors.

1. Two misspelled words
2. An incorrectly used verb and a verb that does not agree with its subject
3. A parenthetical element that is not set off by punctuation

Identifying Run-on Sentences

It can be hard to distinguish run-on sentences from compound sentences. One way to tell them apart is by looking at the two separate ideas in the sentence. Are they connected by a conjunction or a semicolon? If so, they form a compound sentence. If they are connected by a comma or no punctuation at all, they form a run-on sentence.

LESSON 5 YOU TRY IT

Activity 5A *Writing an Informative Essay*

Choose one of the following prompts and write an essay using the steps outlined in this chapter. Then use the checklist to make sure your writing conforms to the Characteristics of Good Writing.

A. Finding A Job	B. Comparing Educational Systems
Write a well-developed essay explaining the process of finding a job, including the steps of writing a résumé and interviewing. Conduct research on the topic and use this evidence in your paper. Organize your writing in a logical way, using headers or other formatting to make main ideas clear.	American students have scored poorly compared to other countries on recent international tests, such as the TIMSS and PIRLS. Choose a country that outscored the United States and compare its educational system with America's. Include a graph or table that visually explains key facts or statistics.

Checklist

Use the following checklist to edit your essay.

My writing has . . .	
DEVELOPMENT	❑ a clear thesis statement ❑ strong supporting points ❑ relevant information based upon research
ORGANIZATION	❑ a clear introduction, body, and conclusion ❑ good transitions ❑ a logical order
EVIDENCE	❑ strong, relevant textual evidence ❑ direct quotations or paraphrased information from other texts
LANGUAGE & STYLE	❑ precise, appropriate word choice ❑ a formal, objective tone
GRAMMAR, SPELLING, & PUNCTUATION	❑ standard grammar ❑ correct spelling ❑ proper punctuation

Steps for Writing an Informative Essay

1. Understand the prompt.
2. Take notes on the sources.
3. Write a thesis statement.
4. Organize your ideas.
5. Develop a complete outline.
6. Write the draft.
7. Revise your essay.
8. Edit and proofread your essay.

Chapter 4

Reporting on Research

In a research report, you gather information from multiple sources to help you answer a question or solve a problem. This process of combining information from different sources into one report is called **synthesizing.**

LESSON 1 TOPICS FOR RESEARCH

The question or problem to research might be identified for you by your teacher or by a prompt on a test. Or you may be given a general subject and asked to generate the specific topic yourself. A good topic is

- broad enough that you can easily find multiple sources about it

- narrow enough that you can cover it in the time you have available to research and write

- focused clearly in its approach to the topic (e.g., comparative, biographical, historical, textual, etc.)

- phrased fairly and objectively so that it does not show a strong bias

Following are sample topics for a five-page research report:

Questions to Answer	Problems to Solve
Where is the line between free speech and cyberbullying?	Avoiding getting laid off in a slow economy
Why are some social media more popular than others?	Increase in autism around the world since the 1990s

> **Fairness in Phrasing**
>
> A good question for research allows for more than one reasonable answer. "Why is math a waste of time?" is not a good question because it indicates that the writer already has a strong bias about the topic.

Activity 1A Phrasing a Research Question

Select the question that is phrased best for a research project. Then explain your choice.

A. What is cyberbullying?

B. How many teens are cyberbullied each year?

C. What are the risks of cyberbullying for the victim and the perpetrator?

_____

_____

_____

_____

Activity 1B Selecting a Question or Problem

*Below are some general subjects for a five-page research report.
Underneath each are three possible questions or problems to address in
the report. Place a check in the column to indicate which of the three is
too broad, which is right in scope, and which is too narrow.*

Question or Problem	Too Broad	Right Scope	Too Narrow
1. General Subject: Questions About the Job Market			
A. To which country did the U.S. lose the most jobs last year?			
B. Which careers in technology will be most affected by outsourcing in the next five years?			
C. Which occupations in the U.S. will likely be lost in the next five years?			
2. General Subject: Questions About College Admissions			
A. Are my grades high enough to get into a public university in my state today?			
B. Are students better prepared for college today than they were 30 years ago?			
C. What guidelines do colleges in the United States today use to decide which applicants to admit?			
3. General Subject: Careers in Fitness			
A. What does an athletic trainer do?			
B. Should I become an athletic trainer or a physical therapist?			
C. What is the difference between an athletic trainer and a physical therapist?			

Discuss with a Partner

Talking with a classmate about possible research topics can help you decide whether you need to narrow or broaden the scope of your report. During your discussion, consider the nature of the assignment, required page length, and availability of sources.

LESSON 2 RELEVANT INFORMATION

Sources may be literary or informational, print or digital, words or images. However, sources must always be relevant and authoritative.

- **Relevant sources** include information that is useful for your report.
- **Authoritative sources** are produced by knowledgeable and trustworthy individuals.

Take notes from your sources so that you can remember the ideas and where the ideas came from. For a classroom assignment, you might want to use notecards to help you organize your ideas and synthesize information. For a test, you might be able to write on the sources that are provided to you.

Activity 2A Identifying Relevant Sources

For each type of source, place a star by the source that would be more useful for a research report on efforts to stop students from texting while driving. Write an explanation in the third column.

Source 1	Source 2	Explanation
1. Web sites		
a site advertising a smart phone app that disables the phone when in motion	a government-run site with statistics pertaining to distracted driving	
2. Books		
Driver Distraction: Theory, Effect, and Mitigation, a nonfiction book by Michael E. Regan, John D. Lee, and Kristie L. Young	*Flirtexting, How to Text Your Way into His Heart,* a self-help book by Debra Goldstein	
3. News articles		
"Local Student Dies While Texting" appearing in your local newspaper	"Distracted Driving Study: Cell Phones, Dialing, Texting Dangerous" appearing on CBS News' Web site	

Activity 2B Evaluating Reliability

Rate the reliability of each person on the subject of texting while driving. Use a scale of 1—not reliable to 5—very reliable. Then review your answers and write a description of what makes a source reliable.

_____ A. A friend who never texts while driving

_____ B. A spokesperson for the Federal Communications Commission

_____ C. A mother who runs a foundation named for her daughter who was killed in a car accident

_____ D. A teacher who believes students should not be permitted to text in school

_____ E. A classmate who wrote a research report about distracted driving

_____ F. Your state Department of Transportation Web site

_____ G. A blogger who writes about the latest mobile phones

_____ H. A state highway patrol officer

> **Collaborate to Evaluate Reliability**
>
> When researching a controversial topic, it may be tempting to use unreliable sources simply because they agree with your opinion. If you are uncertain whether to use a source, discuss it with people who do not share your viewpoint.

What makes a source reliable?

_____

_____

_____

_____

_____

_____

 Activity 2C Interpreting Sources

Read the following excerpt and answer the questions on the next page.

> Each day in the United States, more than 9 people are killed and more than 1,060 people are injured in crashes that are reported to involve a distracted driver. Distracted driving is driving while doing another activity that takes your attention away from driving. Distracted driving can increase the chance of a motor vehicle crash.

continued on next page

continued from previous page

The three main types of distraction include

- Visual: taking your eyes off the road
- Manual: taking your hands off the wheel; and
- Cognitive: taking your mind off of driving.

Distracted driving activities include things like using a cell phone, texting, and eating. Using in-vehicle technologies (such as navigation systems) can also be sources of distraction. While any of these distractions can endanger the driver and others, texting while driving is especially dangerous because it combines all three types of distraction.

Source: "Distracted Driving." Injury Prevention and Control: Motor Vehicle Safety. Centers for Disease Control and Prevention. *cdc.gov.* Web. 13 February 2014.

Part A

Circle the letter before the sentence that best expresses the writer's main idea about distracted driving.

a. When drivers text, they are distracted.

b. Driving distractions can be visual, manual, or cognitive.

c. Distracted driving is driving while doing another activity.

d. Distracted driving causes many vehicle crashes.

Part B

Circle the letter before the two statements that provide direct evidence for the writer's key idea about distracted driving.

a. "Each day in the United States, more than 9 people are killed"

b. "more than 1,060 people are injured in crashes that are reported to involve a distracted driver"

c. "The three main types of distraction include"

d. "Using in-vehicle technologies (such as navigation systems) can also be sources of distraction"

e. "texting while driving is especially dangerous because it combines all three types of distraction."

Two-Part Questions

Tests may include questions about vocabulary or key ideas followed by a question that asks you to identify the evidence for the answer you provided. These questions may be labeled Part A and Part B.

LESSON 3 NOTES FROM SOURCES

Take accurate notes from your sources, recording important ideas to use in your paper. Record notes in a notebook, on cards, or in a computer file. Three basic types of note-taking include:

Summary

Condense a longer passage (or Web page) into a shortened version. Use your own words.

> On the distraction.gov Web site, users can view pictures of children killed or injured by distracted drivers, including five-year-old Xzavier David-Bilbo who was paralyzed after being struck by young driver who was texting. ("Faces," distraction.gov)

Paraphrase

Restate information in your own words.

> Because behavior while driving a passenger car falls under the jurisdiction of individual states, the Federal government can't officially ban texting while driving. ("FAQ," distraction.gov)

Quotation

Record a statement word for word from a source using quotation marks. This will help you avoid plagiarism, or taking credit for something someone else wrote.

> "Sending or reading a text takes your eyes off the road for 4.6 seconds. At 55 mph, that's like driving the length of an entire football field, blindfolded." ("FAQ," distraction.gov)

With each note, record information that will help you identify the source, such as the Web site and section, the author's last name, or the title. <u>Always</u> include the page number for print sources (e.g. "Distracted Driving" 19).

Activity 3A Taking Notes

Take two notes—one a quotation and the other a paraphrase—from the sources on pp. 52–53. Record the source information.

Quotation:

_____

_____

_____

Paraphrase:

_____

_____

_____

_____

Practice Taking Notes

To take notes successfully, you need to identify important information. You can practice this skill every time you read. For example, when you read a story about a football game or a review of a movie, underline the main ideas and circle the most useful details and evidence.

Summarize, Paraphrase, or Quote?

Summarize a source if it has good general ideas, but few useful details.

Paraphrase a source if it has good details, but the specific words used are not that important. Most of your notes should be paraphrases.

Quote a source when the language is effective or memorable or you can't say it better yourself. Use quotations sparingly.

LESSON 4 SYNTHESIZING INFORMATION

The next step is to synthesize and integrate information from your notes into a cohesive paper. First, group notes with similar ideas together. For example, you may have several notes with stories of people who were involved in accidents related to texting and driving. Group these notecards together or paste digital notes onto the same page. Label the notes with a descriptive header, such as "Personal Stories."

As you group your notes, patterns will emerge. You will start to see relationships between big ideas, such as causes and effects or problems and solutions. Thinking about these relationships will help you develop a working outline for a paper.

Activity 4A Categorizing Information

Decide whether each notecard relates to laws against texting and driving or the dangers of texting and driving. Write "Laws" or "Dangers" in the Label column.

Notecard	Label
1. Because behavior while driving a passenger car falls under the jurisdiction of individual states, the Federal government can't officially ban texting while driving. ("FAQ," distraction.gov)	
2. Washington was the first state to pass a texting ban in 2007. Currently, 41 states ban text messaging for all drivers. ("Distracted Driving Laws," ghsa.org)	
3. Eleven percent of drivers aged 18 to 20 who were involved in an automobile accident and survived admitted they were sending or receiving texts when they crashed. (FCC, "Dangers of Texting While Driving")	
4. The Virginia Tech Transportation Institute found that text messaging creates a crash risk 23 times worse than driving while not distracted. (FCC, "Dangers of Texting While Driving")	
5. "Sending or reading a text takes your eyes off the road for 4.6 seconds. At 55 mph, that's like driving the length of an entire football field, blindfolded." (FAQ, distraction.gov)	
6. In California, the fines for fees stemming from a ticket for texting while driving can top $300 for the first offense. (Mukherji,"Texting and Driving: 5 Potential Consequences")	

Carefully and thoughtfully, integrate notes into your report. Your job as a writer is to connect the main ideas together in a logical way. Support the main ideas with the most relevant and convincing information. Your notecards will contain most of the ideas for your paper; however, you will also have to add phrases and sentences that keep the ideas flowing together smoothly.

In the following paragraph, the underlined sentences are from the notes on page 54. Notice how information from the notes fits smoothly into the writing.

> States have taken the lead in stopping distracted driving. <u>Currently, 41 states ban text messaging for all drivers</u> (ghsa. org). However, some states have steeper penalties than others. <u>In California, for example, the fines for texting while driving can top $300 for the first offense</u> (Mukherji).

Activity 4B Synthesizing Ideas

Write a paragraph that synthesizes two of the notes on the dangers of texting and driving from Activity 4A on page 55. Use good transitional words.

_____

_____

_____

_____

_____

_____

_____

_____

_____

_____

_____

_____

_____

_____

_____

Trade Paragraphs

After completing the Synthesizing Ideas paragraph, exchange your paragraph with a classmate. Read each other's answer aloud. Evaluate how the ideas fit together. Offer suggestions on adding more or less information. If direct quotations are included, check for quotation marks.

LESSON 5 CITING SOURCES

Research involves collecting the ideas of others and synthesizing them into something new. This synthesis is very different from **plagiarism,** which is presenting someone else's words as your own. Plagiarism is wrong, and many teachers punish it severely. You can avoid plagiarism if you use

- citations to give credit to your sources
- quotation marks when you use another writer's exact words

Citations

A **citation** is a note in a text that identifies the source of information. There are many acceptable ways to cite sources. This handbook uses the Modern Language Association (MLA) format. According to MLA, any information, statistic, or idea that is not common knowledge and is not your own must be cited in parenthesis by including

- the writer's last name and page number (Gonzolas 178)
- If the writer is not listed, the first word of the title is noted in parentheses ("Dangers" 178)
- If the source has no page numbers, they are omitted from the citation. ("Dangers")

For example, consider this paraphrased sentence:

> While companies producing software, movies, and music cry for laws protecting them from piracy, no one seems to agree on a clear definition of the word (Johns 6).

The citation indicates that the information came from page 6 of a book by an author whose last name is Johns. The author's full name (Adrian Johns), the book title (*Piracy: The Intellectual Property Wars from Gutenberg to Gates*), and other information about the book should appear on a page of sources entitled Works Cited at the end of a report.

Quotations

If you repeat a statement word for word from a source, enclose the words in quotation marks and cite your source. If you introduce the quotation with the author's name, just include the page number in the citation. For example:

> Scientist John Houghton estimates that "the global average temperature will rise by about a third of a degree Celsius or more every ten years" (26).

Paraphrases

If you phrase information in your own words, you still must cite your source in parenthesis. Do not use quotation marks around your paraphrase. Failing to cite paraphrases is plagiarism.

Citations on Tests

Citations may not be required for essays on tests. However, including them is a good habit. By indicating your sources, you can easily go back to them if you need to.

Citing E-books

Citing e-books presents a problem because some do not have page numbers. List the author's name and the chapter or other section. Place a comma between the author's last name and the abbreviation *ch.* (Johns, ch. 2)

Works Cited

A works cited page is a list of all the sources used in your paper, written in the following general format:

Last name, First name. Title of work. City of Publisher: Publisher, Year of Publication. Medium of Publication.

Works Cited entry for a book:

Johns, Adrian. *Piracy: The Intellectual Property Wars from Gutenberg to Gates*. Chicago: University Chicago, 2009. Print.

Works Cited entry for an article on a Web page:

Strauss, Karsten. "TV and Film Piracy: Threatening an Industry?" *Forbes*. Forbes Magazine. 06 Mar. 2013. Web. 01 Jan. 2014.

Activity 5A Citing Sources

Read this excerpt, taken from page 23 of the book Global Warming *by John Houghton. Then complete the activities below.*

> We know for sure that because of human activities, especially the burning of fossil fuel, coal, oil, and gas, together with widespread deforestation, the gas carbon dioxide has been emitted into the atmosphere in increasing amounts over the past 200 years and more substantially over the past 50 years. Every year these emissions currently add to the carbon already present in the atmosphere a further 8,000 million tons, much of which is likely to remain there for a period of 100 years or more.

Periods and Citations

When a citation falls at the end of a sentence, place the period after the citation.

1. Write a sentence that uses a direct quotation from the excerpt. Identify the author in the sentence. Include a citation.

_____

_____

_____

Collaborate with Quotations

Interview a partner about a book the individual has read, and then write a summary of the interview. Include at least two direct quotations and two indirect quotations in your summary.

2. Write a sentence that paraphrases information from the excerpt by Houghton. Identify the author in a citation.

_____

_____

_____

LESSON 6 HOW TO WRITE A RESEARCH REPORT

Following is a model demonstrating six steps for writing a research report. Use these steps to help you write your own reports.

Step 1. Understand the prompt.

Begin by reading the directions closely. The directions that explain what to write about are called a **prompt.**

- The prompt might describe a general topic, such as school discipline codes. You will need to narrow the subject to a topic you can cover in your report.

- The prompt might already be very well defined. It may come either before or after the sources that will provide the textual evidence you will use in your report.

Activity 6A Analyzing the Prompt

Summarize the following prompt in your own words.

At Gettysburg, President Lincoln said America's democracy can only survive if it is "of the people, by the people, and for the people." Today, politicians talk of maintaining openness, or transparency, in the government to allow citizens to oversee the actions and decisions of those they elect to represent them. How transparent is our government? Use the information in the sources that follow to write a report that answers this question.

_____

_____

_____

_____

_____

Step 2. Take notes on the sources.

Whether the sources are provided for you on a test or you find your own, take notes on them with your purpose in mind.

- Underline key statements in the source.

- To help you find the notes later, write a brief note in the margin identifying the point of the underlined text. The next activity includes a model.

> ### Interpreting the Prompt
>
> Many students score poorly on tests because they do not read the prompt carefully enough. For example, think of the difference between a prompt that asks you to *describe* your school and one that asks you to *evaluate* your school.

> ### Best Practices for Taking Notes
>
> Using paper or electronic notecards to store and organize your ideas is a good practice, especially for papers longer than two pages. Record one idea, piece of evidence, or bit of information per card. Next, write the topic and possible sub-topics on the first line of each card. Doing so will help you group common information and organize your essay. Be sure to note the source as well.

Activity 6B *Underlining and Adding Notes*

Take notes on the following sources by underlining key statements and adding notes in the margin. One note is done for you as a model.

Source 1

"Man Behind NSA Leaks Says He Did It to Safeguard Privacy, Liberty" by Barbara Starr and Holly Yan

He's a high school dropout who worked his way into the most <u>secretive computers in U.S. intelligence as a defense contractor</u>—only to blow those secrets wide open by spilling details of classified surveillance programs.

Now, Edward Snowden might never live in the United States as a free man again. Where he may end up was a source of global speculation Sunday after he flew from Hong Kong to Russia, his ultimate destination unknown to most.

Snowden has revealed himself as the source of documents outlining a massive effort by the U.S. National Security Agency to track cell phone calls and <u>monitor the e-mail and Internet traffic of virtually all Americans</u>.

Snowden, 29, said he just wanted the public to know what the government was doing. "Even if you're not doing anything wrong you're being watched and recorded," he said.

Snowden told *The Guardian* newspaper in the United Kingdom that he had access to the full rosters of everyone working at the NSA, the entire intelligence community and undercover assets around the world.

Should the government be able to keep some secrets in order to protect citizens from terrorism?

Source 2

"Transparency and Open Government"
excerpted from President Obama's memorandum to heads of executive departments and agencies

SUBJECT: Transparency and Open Government

My Administration is committed to creating an unprecedented level of openness in Government. We will work together to ensure the public trust and establish a system of transparency, public participation, and collaboration. Openness will strengthen our democracy and promote efficiency and effectiveness in Government.

Government should be transparent. Transparency promotes accountability and provides information for citizens about what their Government is doing. Information maintained by the Federal Government is a national asset. My Administration will take appropriate action, consistent with law and policy, to disclose information rapidly in forms that the public can readily find and use. Executive departments and agencies should harness new technologies to put information about their operations and decisions online and readily available to the public. Executive departments and agencies should also solicit public feedback to identify information of greatest use to the public.

Source: Obama, Barack. "Transparency and Open Government." The White House. *whitehouse.gov*. n.d. Web. 21 Jan. 2014. <http://www.whitehouse.gov/the_press_office/TransparencyandOpenGovernment>.

Source 3

"What is FOIA?"

The Freedom of Information Act (FOIA) is a law that gives you the right to access information from the federal government. It is often described as the law that keeps citizens in the know about their government.

Source: "What Is FOIA?" *FOIA.gov.* N.p., n.d. Web. 23 Jan. 2014. <http://www.foia.gov/>.

Source 4

"Protection from Discrimination"
excerpted from the DWPP home page

OSHA's Whistleblower Protection Program enforces the whistleblower provisions of more than twenty whistleblower statutes protecting employees who report violations of various workplace safety, airline, commercial motor carrier, consumer product, environmental, financial reform, food safety, health insurance reform, motor vehicle safety, nuclear, pipeline, public transportation agency, railroad, maritime, and securities laws. Rights afforded by these whistleblower acts include, but are not limited to, worker participation in safety and health activities, reporting a work-related injury, illness or fatality, or reporting a violation of the statutes.

Protection from discrimination means that an employer cannot retaliate by taking "adverse action" against workers, such as:

- Firing or laying off
- Blacklisting
- Demoting
- Denying overtime or promotion
- Disciplining
- Denial of benefits
- Failure to hire or rehire
- Intimidation
- Making threats
- Reassignment affecting prospects for promotion
- Reducing pay or hours

Source: "The Whistleblowers Protection Programs." Directorate of the Whistleblower Protection Program. www.*whistleblowers.gov.* n.d. Web. 21 Jan. 2014.

Source 5

"Greenwald: NSA Leaker Snowden Has No Whistleblower Protection"
excerpted from *Politifact*

In the view of Glenn Greenwald, the investigative journalist who was one of the first to gain access to Snowden's stolen documents, a fair trial is the last thing that awaits the whistleblower if he comes back without a deal.

"Under the Espionage Act, you're not allowed to come into court and say 'I was justified in disclosing this information'," Greenwald said on CNN's *The Lead*. "There is no whistleblower exception in the Espionage Act."

Greenwald's debate with Ruth Marcus of the *Washington Post* made for good television. But we wanted to dig deeper into Greenwald's point about Snowden. There are two pieces to this puzzle. What does the law say and could Snowden reasonably expect to tell his side of the story in a trial?

Limited protections for the intelligence community

The Espionage Act of 1917 makes it a crime punishable by death or imprisonment to share "information relating to the national defense" with anyone who might want to do harm to the United States. Snowden faces two counts of unauthorized communication under that law.

Source: "Greenwald: NSA Leaker Snowden Has No Whistleblower Protection." PunditFact. *PolitiFact.com* N.p., n.d. Web. 23 Jan. 2014. Copyright PolitiFact.com.

Source 6

Remarks by the President on Review of Signals Intelligence

Now, the reforms I'm proposing today should give the American people greater confidence that their rights are being protected, even as our intelligence and law enforcement agencies maintain the tools they need to keep us safe. And I recognize that there are additional issues that require further debate. For example, some who participated in our review, as well as some members of Congress, would like to see more sweeping reforms to the use of national security

continued on next page

continued from previous page

letters so that we have to go to a judge each time before issuing these requests. Here, I have concerns that we should not set a standard for terrorism investigations that is higher than those involved in investigating an ordinary crime. But I agree that greater oversight on the use of these letters may be appropriate, and I'm prepared to work with Congress on this issue. . . .

. . . the new presidential directive that I've issued today will clearly prescribe what we do, and do not do, when it comes to our overseas surveillance. To begin with, the directive makes clear that the United States only uses signals intelligence for legitimate national security purposes, and not for the purpose of indiscriminately reviewing the emails or phone calls of ordinary folks. I've also made it clear that the United States does not collect intelligence to suppress criticism or dissent, nor do we collect intelligence to disadvantage people on the basis of their ethnicity, or race, or gender, or sexual orientation, or religious beliefs. . . .

And in terms of our bulk collection of signals intelligence, U.S. intelligence agencies will only use such data to meet specific security requirements: counterintelligence, counterterrorism, counter-proliferation, cybersecurity, force protection for our troops and our allies, and combating transnational crime, including sanctions evasion.

Source: Obama, President Barack. "Remarks by the President on Review of Signals Intelligence." Department of Justice. Washington, D.C. January 17, 2014.

Step 3. Organize your ideas.

Determine the best order in which to present your ideas. The order should be logical so readers can easily follow your train of thought. Making an outline before you write your draft will help you organize your ideas.

A research report, like most other types of texts, is organized into three basic parts. The introduction should introduce the topic and state it clearly, usually in one paragraph. The body should present the research in multiple paragraphs. The conclusion restates the topic and summarizes the research. It should give a sense of closure to the writing.

> **Collaborate about Organization**
>
> Before organizing your information, discuss it with a partner. Talking about what you have researched can help you see the best way to organize it.

Activity 6C Analyzing an Outline

On the next page is an outline for a research report about government transparency. As you read it, mark it as follows:

1. Circle the headings for the portions of the outline that are part of the body.

2. Underline where the research question is stated.

3. Are the main points in the body in logical order? Why or why not?

Sample Outline: The People's Window

Research Question: How transparent is our government?

I. **Introduction**
    A. American's shocked by Operation PRISM
    B. Problems of surveillance and leaked documents

II. **Background and Focus**
    A. Definition of transparency
    B. Role of transparency in a democracy
    C. Focus: How transparent is our government?

III. **Examples of Transparency**
    A. Freedom of Information Act
    B. Government Accountability Project

IV. **Analysis**
    A. Limitations on transparency
    B. Consequences for exceeding limits

V. **Conclusion**
    A. Full circle: Operation Prism
    B. Future implications of limited government transparency

Step 4. Write the draft.

Below is a draft of the report. It is based on the outline and the notes taken on the sources. Please note that the draft contains some mistakes you will correct in a later activity.

Activity 6D Analyzing a Draft

Following is the draft of an essay. Mark it as follows:

1. In the margin beside the first sentence, write a phrase to indicate whether you think the opening is effective.

2. Evaluate the use of sources. If any in-text citations are needed, make a note in the margin.

3. Place a checkmark above three specific pieces of evidence from the sources.

4. Circle three transitional words or phrases.

5. Draw a box around headings that show the organization of the essay.

6. In the margin beside the last sentence, write a phrase to indicate whether you think it is effective.

Sample Draft: The People's Window

How would you feel if you discovered the government tracked each cell phone number you dialed, every Internet site you visited, and all the e-mail you sent? That is in fact what America's secret data gathering program, code-named PRISM, was designed to do as a way of combating the war on terrorism (Starr and Yan). Americans were freaked out to hear of PRISMs details and other clandestine government practices threw documents leaked in 2013 by federal contractor Edward Snowden, who fled the country fearing severe consequences.

Four years earlier, on his first day in office, President Barak Obama publicly stated his commitment to "creating an unprecedented level of openness in Government. We will work together to ensure the public trust and establish a system of transparency" to provide "information for citizens about what their Government is doing" ("Memorandum"). Indeed, to prevent the government from abusing its powers, citizens are responsible for overseeing its actions. Such oversight is only possible if the government maintains a window for public scrutiny. While the U.S. government attempts to maintain this window, for some, it is not transparent enough.

Examples of Transparency

The Freedom of Information Act is one means of transparency. Enacted by Congress in 1966, this law "gives you the right to access information from the federal government. It is often described as the law that keeps citizens in the know about their government" ("What"). Upon request, state and federal documents are available to anyone who asks. If a citizen knows the information she is looking for, FOIA ensures she may have it.

Another way the government maintains transparency is through the Government Accountability Project (GAP), which oversees a series of "whistleblower" protection laws. A *whistleblower* is a private or federal employee who

continued on next page

continued from previous page

reports workplace wrongdoing. Without legal protection against "firing or laying off, blacklisting, demoting, denying overtime or promotion, . . . making threats," etc., they would be less likely to offer up information on co-workers' illegal practices or policies ("Whistleblowers"). After verifying the truth of such reports, GAP tries to find solutions to improve the situation.

Limitations on Transparency

If the Freedom of Information Act gave a whistleblower like Edward Snowden a legal way to access government documents and the Government Accountability Project gave him protection from retaliation, why would he circumvent the system by stealing government documents and then fleeing in fear? Perhaps because complete transparency is not always in the public's best interest. In fact, any document that "would be harmful to governmental or private interests" cannot be released under FOIA ("What").

Additionally, the Espionage Act of 1917 provides severe ramifications and no protection for those who share "'information relating to the national defense' with anyone who might want to do harm to the United States'" ("Greenwald"). Consequences are even more severe for members of the military—they risk the death penalty for providing classified information to the enemy.

In a healthy democracy, upstanding citizens are supposed to be keeping an eye on the government, not the other way around. Nonetheless, "even if you're not doing anything wrong you're being watched and recorded," claims Snowden (Star and Yan). While the government indeed promotes some openness and accountability to the public, "transparency" is not a suitable term. Even our own laws restrict the government from maintaining an absolutely clear window into its inner workings.

continued on next page

continued from previous page

While some information pertaining to terrorist threats is best kept under wraps, the government soiled its reputation by justifying a wide-sweeping secret program like PRISM. In fact, following Snowden's revelations, President Obama initiated a series of reforms to clean up how the government collects data on U.S. citizens. Obama stated the changes to PRISM "should give the American people greater confidence that their rights are being protected, even as our intelligence and law enforcement agencies maintain the tools they need to keep us safe" ("Remarks"). Despite the President's reassurances, however, our window into the government remains smudged.

But perhaps it is a little less dirty.

Works Cited

"Greenwald: NSA Leaker Snowden Has No Whistleblower Protection." politifact.com. Tampa Bay Times, n.d. Web. 23 Jan. 2014.

Starr, Barbara and Holly Yan. "Man Behind NSA Leaks Says He Did It to Safeguard Privacy, Liberty." *CNN*. Cable News Network, 23 June 2013. Web. 23 Jan. 2014.

Obama, President Barack. "President's Memorandum on Transparency and Open Government—Interagency Collaboration." *whitehouse.gov*. The White House, Feb. 24, 2009. Web. 21 Jan. 2014.

---. "Remarks by the President on Review of Signals Intelligence." Department of Justice. Washington, D.C. January 17, 2014. Web. 24 Jan. 2014.

---. "Transparency and Open Government." *whitehouse.gov*. The White House, n.d. Web. 21 Jan. 2014.

"What Is FOIA?" *FOIA.gov*. United States Department of Justice, n.d. Web. 23 Jan. 2014.

"The Whistleblower Protection Programs." *whistleblowers.gov*. Directorate of the Whistleblower Protection Program, n.d. Web. 21 Jan. 2014.

Step 5. Revise your essay.

Good writers use similar grammatical patterns in their sentences to emphasize relationships among ideas. Parallel structure brings order, clarity, and rhythm to your sentences. Check for parallel structure whenever you draw a comparison, highlight a difference, or list items in a series. The connecting words that signal the need for parallel structure can be remembered by the mnemonic device **BANANO**: **B**(oth) **A**(nd) **N**(ot only/but also) **A**(s well as), **N**(either/nor) and **O**(r). Study the following sentence:

> I might like to pursue a career in medicine, art, or defending people in court.

If you read the sentence aloud, you will hear that the sentence's ideas are not phrased using the same grammatical pattern. It uses two nouns, *medicine* and *art*, yet ends with a noun phrase—*defending people in court*. Because the sentence connects three ideas using the word *or*, it requires parallel structure. Revised, the sentence reads,

> I might like to pursue a career in medicine, art, or law.

Activity 6E Using Parallel Structure

Rewrite each sentence so it uses the same grammatical pattern to connect related ideas:

1. Monet, Renoir, and Mary Cassatt were three impressionist painters.

   _____

   _____

   _____

2. The film that she wrote, directed the actors in, and promoted is now available on DVD.

   _____

   _____

   _____

3. He has traveled to Alaska, California, as well as seeing two states in New England.

   _____

   _____

   _____

Online Peer Revision

Post your research report online, share it with a classmate, and ask them to evaluate your use of sources. Have them use the comment feature to make suggestions and offer positive feedback.

Collaboration on Parallel Structure

A good place to use parallel structure is in your research paper's thesis statement.

For example: *Both risky lending and easy credit contributed to the Great Recession.*

Working with a partner, review the incomplete thesis statements below. Discuss several reasonable responses peer each blank and then come to a consensus. Next, identify the underlying grammatical pattern. In the blank, write your final answer in parallel form.

- Global warming harms plants, animals, and _____.

- Cyberbullying and _____ should not be protected as free speech under the Constitution.

4. The student's writing was neither clear nor an interesting essay to read.

_____

_____

_____

5. I had a cat, she had a dog, and we both were allergic to animals.

_____

_____

_____

6. On the other hand, both running in the city and skiing can be dangerous.

_____

_____

7. Students have a right to free speech—but shouldn't disrupt the learning of others. Schools can punish students—but not to take away all of their rights.

_____

_____

_____

_____

_____

_____

Varying Syntax

When writing, try to vary the syntax, or the way words and phrases are arranged. Overusing a simple subject-verb pattern results in boring writing. Think about using subordinate clauses, noun phrases, and prepositional phrases to add life to sentences. Compare these examples:

- We ate buttery popcorn at the movie.
- While watching the movie, we ate buttery popcorn.
- At the movies, we ate buttery popcorn.
- Watching a movie, we ate buttery popcorn.
- Eating buttery popcorn, we watched the movie.

Think about whether eating or watching is emphasized in each one based upon what ideas are placed in subordinate clauses.

Tufte's *Artful Sentences* is a good resource to help you vary the syntax of your sentences.

Step 6. Edit and proofread your essay.

After revising your paper, proofread it carefully, looking for mistakes in diction (word choice), spelling, punctuation, and grammar. Paying close attention to these final details helps convey professionalism. After spell-checking your essay, examine it closely for commonly confused words such as *then/than, too/to, its/it's,* and *there/they're.* Often, spelling-checkers will not flag these words, so it is up to you to find them.

> Congress has passed laws limiting the rights of people who lie too encourage violence.

The mistake is that the word *too* is used incorrectly. *Too* means "also," which clearly is not the intent of the writer in this sentence.

> **Confusing Verbs:**
> ***Affect* Versus *Effect***
> ....
>
> *Affect* is a verb.
>
> Don't let her negative attitude affect you.
>
> *Effect* is a noun.
>
> The effect of her negative attitude was that no one wanted to be her friend.

 ### Activity 6F *Correcting Commonly Confused Words*

Circle the word(s) used incorrectly in the following sentences. Write the correct word(s) on the lines.

1. Its sometimes overwhelming to look to the heavens since their are to many stars to count.

   _____

   _____

2. Because his school is further away than he would like, he prefers to bicycle rather then walk.

   _____

   _____

3. I didn't chose to loose my cell phone. It was an accident.

   _____

   _____

4. At halftime the coach adviced us not to lay down and except defeat.

   _____

   _____

Activity 6G Proofreading an Essay

Rewrite the introduction to the essay, correcting informal language, punctuation, and incorrect words.

How would you feel if you discovered the government tracked each cell phone number you dialed, every Internet site you visited, and all the e-mail you sent? That is in fact what America's secret data gathering program, code-named PRISM, was designed to do to help combat the war on terrorism (Starr and Yan). Americans were freaked out to hear of PRISMs details and other clandestine government practices threw documents leaked in 2013 by federal contractor Edward Snowden, who fled the country fearing severe consequences.

_____

_____

_____

_____

_____

_____

_____

_____

_____

_____

_____

_____

_____

_____

_____

_____

Formal vs. Informal Writing

After you write a draft, read it aloud. You will probably hear missing words and awkward phrasing. Listen carefully for colloquialisms, or informal expressions that are not appropriate for formal research papers in academic settings. This includes slang terms such as *awesome*. Another common mistake is to use personal pronouns such as *I* or *you*. Third-person pronouns are appropriate (they, she, him), but first- and second-person pronouns are not.

LESSON 7 YOU TRY IT

Now it is your turn to write a research report. Use the steps outlined in this chapter to guide you as you write.

Step 1. Understand the prompt.

Step 2. Take notes on sources.

Step 3. Organize your ideas.

Step 4. Write the draft.

Step 5. Revise your essay.

Step 6. Edit and proofread your essay.

Activity 7A Writing a Research Report

Write a research report in response to one of the following prompts.

A. Renewable Energy Proposal	B. Supreme Court Decisions
Your school is considering either installing a wind turbine or solar panels to generate power for their buildings. Research the advantages and disadvantages of these two alternative forms of renewable energy for your school. End your report with a preliminary recommendation about which option is a better fit for your school. Use information from at least four sources in your report and use MLA format for citations.	Choose a landmark Supreme Court case. (See uscourts.gov for ideas.) Research the facts in the case and the process by which it came to be heard by the Supreme Court. Explain how the Court's decision impacted subsequent cases. Use information from at least four sources in your report and use MLA format for citations.

My writing has . . .	
DEVELOPMENT	❏ a clear question to answer or problem to solve ❏ a topic appropriate to the length of the report
ORGANIZATION	❏ a clear introduction, body, and conclusion ❏ good transitions to maintain the flow of ideas ❏ logical order
EVIDENCE	❏ strong, relevant textual evidence ❏ information from multiple authoritative sources
LANGUAGE & STYLE	❏ precise, appropriate word choice ❏ a formal, objective tone
GRAMMAR, SPELLING, & PUNCTUATION	❏ standard grammar ❏ correct spelling ❏ proper punctuation

Chapter 5

Writing a Literary Analysis

When you write a **summary** of a book, you briefly state the main idea and most important details. An **analysis** goes deeper than a summary by examining the book and interpreting its content. Summarizing and analyzing are valuable skills for both college and the workplace. Many people, for example, need to read books to keep up with changes in their field—and being able to summarize and analyze texts is essential.

> **Types of Literature**
>
> Writing assessments may ask you to read and respond to poetry, drama, or a short story.

LESSON 1 ELEMENTS OF A LITERARY ANALYSIS

A literary analysis requires you to look at specific elements of a work of literature. Here are some commonly used literary devices found in stories and poems and how you might be asked to write about them in an essay.

Definitions of Literary Elements	A prompt may ask you to analyze how . . .
Characterization: description of the characters in the story	• characters are introduced and developed • characters' choices develop the plot and theme
Plot: events in the story	• events in the story influence the characters • the events build upon each other • the order of events impacts the story
Structure: arrangement of lines of poetry or the order in which ideas and events are presented	• the author's choices of where to begin or end a story supports the overall structure • a comedic or tragic resolution impacts the reader
Setting: where and when the events take place	• the setting influences the plot and the characters' choices
Language: word choice and figurative language	• words and phrases impact meaning and tone
Point of View: who is narrating the events or the author's viewpoint	• point of view is related to satire, sarcasm, irony, or understatement
Theme: central idea of a text	• two or more themes interact and build upon each other • two passages from the same time period treat similar themes or topics

> **Collaboration on Figurative Language**
>
> In a small group, develop three examples of each type of figurative language described below.
>
> • **Verbal irony** is a difference between what is said and what is meant, often resulting in **sarcasm**. Example: "I'm really looking forward to my root canal today."
>
> • **Dramatic irony** is when the audience (or reader) knows something the characters don't know. Example: Romeo thinks Juliet is dead so he kills himself; however, Juliet is merely sleeping.
>
> • **Situational irony** is a difference between what is expected and what actually happens. Example: In "Gift of the Magi," a husband pawns his pocket watch to buy combs for his wife's hair, only to discover that she has cut her hair to buy him a watch chain.

Activity 1A *Understanding Literary Devices*

Choose a work of literature you have read recently. Complete the following tasks to help you analyze the work.

Title: _____

1. Describe the main characters.

_____
_____
_____

2. Summarize the plot.

_____
_____
_____
_____
_____

3. Describe the setting.

_____
_____

4. Identify the tone.

_____
_____

5. Identify the point of view.

_____
_____

6. Explain the theme.

_____
_____

7. Give examples of two types of figurative language used.

_____
_____
_____

LESSON 2 EVIDENCE FROM TEXTS

Before you write an essay, you will be asked to read a work of literature such as a short story or poem. Watch for important details in the writing; underline key sentences that describe the characters and reveal the theme of the work.

If you are taking a writing assessment, you may be asked to explain key words or phrases, write a summary, or find evidence to support the main ideas before writing an essay. Answering these questions correctly will help you accurately interpret the literature in your literary analysis.

> **Paying Close Attention**
>
> As you read a work of literature, take notes about anything that strikes you. For example, underline words that describe characters or explain their feelings or motivations. Comment on figurative language, unusual words, or changes of direction in the plot. Use your notes to help you analyze the text.

Activity 2A *Answering Questions About a Work of Literature*

Read the following short story and answer the questions that follow.

The Open Window by Saki (H.H. Munro)

"My aunt will be down presently, Mr. Nuttel," said a very self-possessed young lady of fifteen; "in the meantime you must try and put up with me."

Framton Nuttel endeavoured to say the correct something which should duly flatter the niece of the moment without unduly discounting the aunt that was to come. Privately he doubted more than ever whether these formal visits on a succession of total strangers would do much towards helping the nerve cure which he was supposed to be undergoing.

"I know how it will be," his sister had said when he was preparing to migrate to this rural retreat; "you will bury yourself down there and not speak to a living soul, and your nerves will be worse than ever from moping. I shall just give you letters of introduction to all the people I know there. Some of them, as far as I can remember, were quite nice."

Framton wondered whether Mrs. Sappleton, the lady to whom he was presenting one of the letters of introduction came into the "nice" division.

"Do you know many of the people round here?" asked the niece, when she judged that they had had sufficient silent communion.

"Hardly a soul," said Framton. "My sister was staying here, at the rectory, you know, some four years ago, and she gave me letters of introduction to some of the people here."

He made the last statement in a tone of distinct regret.

"Then you know practically nothing about my aunt?" pursued the self-possessed young lady.

"Only her name and address," admitted the caller. He was wondering whether Mrs. Sappleton was in the married or widowed state. An undefinable something about the room seemed to suggest masculine habitation.

"Her great tragedy happened just three years ago," said the child; "that would be since your sister's time."

continued on next page

---

continued from previous page

"Her tragedy?" asked Framton; somehow in this restful country spot tragedies seemed out of place.

"You may wonder why we keep that window wide open on an October afternoon," said the niece, indicating a large French window that opened on to a lawn.

"It is quite warm for the time of the year," said Framton; "but has that window got anything to do with the tragedy?"

"Out through that window, three years ago to a day, her husband and her two young brothers went off for their day's shooting. They never came back. In crossing the moor to their favourite snipe-shooting ground they were all three engulfed in a treacherous piece of bog. It had been that dreadful wet summer, you know, and places that were safe in other years gave way suddenly without warning. Their bodies were never recovered. That was the dreadful part of it." Here the child's voice lost its self-possessed note and became falteringly human. "Poor aunt always thinks that they will come back someday, they and the little brown spaniel that was lost with them, and walk in at that window just as they used to do. That is why the window is kept open every evening till it is quite dusk. Poor dear aunt, she has often told me how they went out, her husband with his white waterproof coat over his arm, and Ronnie, her youngest brother, singing 'Bertie, why do you bound?' as he always did to tease her, because she said it got on her nerves. Do you know, sometimes on still, quiet evenings like this, I almost get a creepy feeling that they will all walk in through that window—"

She broke off with a little shudder. It was a relief to Framton when the aunt bustled into the room with a whirl of apologies for being late in making her appearance.

"I hope Vera has been amusing you?" she said.

"She has been very interesting," said Framton.

"I hope you don't mind the open window," said Mrs. Sappleton briskly; "my husband and brothers will be home directly from shooting, and they always come in this way. They've been out for snipe in the marshes today, so they'll make a fine mess over my poor carpets. So like you menfolk, isn't it?"

She rattled on cheerfully about the shooting and the scarcity of birds, and the prospects for duck in the winter. To Framton it was all purely horrible. He made a desperate but only partially successful effort to turn the talk on to a less ghastly topic, he was conscious that his hostess was giving him only a fragment of her attention, and her eyes were constantly straying past him to the open window and the lawn beyond. It was certainly an unfortunate coincidence that he should have paid his visit on this tragic anniversary.

"The doctors agree in ordering me complete rest, an absence of mental excitement, and avoidance of anything in the nature of violent physical exercise," announced Framton, who laboured under the tolerably widespread delusion that total strangers and chance acquaintances are hungry for the least detail of one's ailments and infirmities, their cause and cure. "On the matter of diet they are not so much in agreement," he continued.

"No?" said Mrs. Sappleton, in a voice

continued on next page

continued from previous page

which only replaced a yawn at the last moment. Then she suddenly brightened into alert attention—but not to what Framton was saying.

"Here they are at last!" she cried. "Just in time for tea, and don't they look as if they were muddy up to the eyes!"

Framton shivered slightly and turned towards the niece with a look intended to convey sympathetic comprehension. The child was staring out through the open window with a dazed horror in her eyes. In a chill shock of nameless fear, Framton swung round in his seat and looked in the same direction.

In the deepening twilight three figures were walking across the lawn towards the window, they all carried guns under their arms, and one of them was additionally burdened with a white coat hung over his shoulders. A tired brown spaniel kept close at their heels. Noiselessly they neared the house, and then a hoarse young voice chanted out of the dusk: "I said, Bertie, why do you bound?"

Framton grabbed wildly at his stick and hat; the hall door, the gravel drive, and the front gate were dimly noted stages in his headlong retreat. A cyclist coming along the road had to run into the hedge to avoid imminent collision.

"Here we are, my dear," said the bearer of the white mackintosh, coming in through the window, "fairly muddy, but most of it's dry. Who was that who bolted out as we came up?"

"A most extraordinary man, a Mr. Nuttel," said Mrs. Sappleton; "could only talk about his illnesses, and dashed off without a word of goodby or apology when you arrived. One would think he had seen a ghost."

"I expect it was the spaniel," said the niece calmly; "he told me he had a horror of dogs. He was once hunted into a cemetery somewhere on the banks of the Ganges by a pack of pariah dogs, and had to spend the night in a newly dug grave with the creatures snarling and grinning and foaming just above him. Enough to make anyone lose their nerve."

Romance at short notice was her speciality.

Part A

Read the following sentence from the story.

Romance at short notice was her speciality.

Based upon the context, the word romance *means—*

a. emotional attraction

b. a medieval legend

c. an outlandish tale

d. a love story

Vocabulary Assessment

Some writing tests will require you to answer multiple-choice questions on a story or poem. Some tests present questions in two parts. The first task asks you to define a key word from the story. The second question asks you to provide context clues that helped you determine the definition.

Part B

Which quotations from the text in Part A best help the reader understand the meaning of the word *romance*?

a. "The doctors agree in ordering me complete rest, an absence of mental excitement, and avoidance of anything in the nature of violent physical exercise," announced Framton,

b. "Out through that window, three years ago to a day, her husband and her two young brothers went off for their day's shooting. They never came back . . ."

c. The child was staring out through the open window with a dazed horror in her eyes.

d. "He was once hunted into a cemetery somewhere on the banks of the Ganges by a pack of pariah dogs . . . "

Activity 2B Identifying Key Ideas

Use your reading of "The Open Window to answer the following questions.

Part A

For most of the story, the reader understands the events from the point of view of which character?

a. Vera

b. Framton

c. Mrs. Sappleton

d. Framton's sister

Part B

Select three pieces of evidence from "The Open Window" that support your answer to Part A.

a. Framton Nuttel endeavoured to say the correct something which should duly flatter the niece of the moment without unduly discounting the aunt that was to come.

b. "Then you know practically nothing about my aunt?" pursued the self-possessed young lady.

c. . . . announced Framton, who laboured under the tolerably widespread delusion that total strangers and chance acquaintances are hungry for the least detail of one's ailments and infirmities . . .

d. It was certainly an unfortunate coincidence that he should have paid his visit on this tragic anniversary.

e. Romance at short notice was her speciality.

> ### Draw Evidence from Literary Texts
>
> Writers indicate the key ideas in their texts through the details they choose to include. If you can't support an idea with details from the text, then it probably isn't one of the text's key ideas.

LESSON 3 HOW TO WRITE A LITERARY ANALYSIS ESSAY

A literary analysis essay will ask you to look for specific elements of the text, such as theme, characters, point of view, or word choice. You will be required to supply textual evidence to support your analysis. The following will help you break down the process of writing a literary analysis into manageable tasks.

Step 1. Understand the prompt.

The directions for writing an essay are called the **prompt.** The verbs in it tell you what to do. Here is an example of a prompt:

> Identify the point of view in "The Open Window." Analyze how this point of view influences the story. Base your analysis on how much access the reader has to the thoughts and feelings of the different characters. Be sure to include specific evidence from the text to support your ideas.

Activity 3A Analyzing a Prompt

In the prompt above, underline two key words or phrases in each sentence. Then finish the following statements:

1. In my literary analysis, I must

_____

_____

2. The kinds of details I should include in my essay are

_____

_____

Step 2. Take notes on the texts.

As you read "The Open Window," you may have underlined some important sentences or written some notes in the margins. Now you should return to the story with the prompt in mind.

- Look for clues that reveal the point of view.
- Find specific examples of how point of view influences the story.
- Organize your notes, possibly using a graphic organizer.

The chart on the next page contains examples of graphic organizers that fit with different writing prompts.

Activity 3B Organizing Notes

The chart below includes notes from "The Open Window." Complete the chart by filling in the blanks in each box.

Point of View: The story is mostly written in _____ point of view from the perspective of the character of_____. However, the point of view shifts when _____ _____.
Examples: How point of view affects how the reader experiences the story.   • At first, the story Vera tells appears to be the truth.   • The reader and Framton both think the window is open because Mrs. Sappleton can't accept the truth about her husband and brothers.   • As Mrs. Sappleton talks about the three men and stares at the open window, it appears to Framton and the reader that _____ _____ _____ _____.   • When the three men return, Framton thinks _____ _____ and the reader views the figures through his terrified eyes.   • After Framton leaves and the narrator stays in the house instead of following Framton, the reader finds out that _____ _____ _____.
Summary: The writer's choice of point of view results in _____ _____ _____ _____

Point of View
....

This prompt assumes that you understand different types of point of view.

First person: Events narrated by a character in the story

Third person, limited omniscient: Events narrated by an outside narrator who knows the thoughts of only the main character

Third person, omniscient: events narrated by an outside narrator with access to multiple characters' thoughts

Step 3. Write a thesis statement.

After gathering notes, write a **thesis statement.** The thesis statement should clearly state the central idea of your literary analysis. It will guide your writing, so it should fit both the prompt and your notes.

Activity 3C Write a Thesis Statement

Finish the sentence to write a strong thesis statement or write your own thesis statement on the lines provided.

1. Because "The Open Window" is written from _____

_____

_____

2. Thesis Statement:

_____

_____

Step 4. Organize your ideas.

Next, think about how you will organize your notes and your thesis statement into a cohesive essay. As you may already know, essays have three main parts: an introduction, a body, and a conclusion.

The introduction should include the title of the text and the author. You may want to summarize the work in one or two sentences. Keep it short. You should also include your thesis statement.

In the body of your essay, develop your thesis statement by stating your conclusions about the literature. How you organize these main points will depend on the prompt you have been given. For the prompt about "The Open Window," you might write three or four body paragraphs with supporting details and examples from the story arranged in chronological order. Remember, each paragraph should be devoted to one central idea that supports and explains your thesis statement.

The conclusion of the essay brings the writing together in a satisfying way. You may include a final thought. You may also restate your thesis statement using different words.

Step 5. Develop a complete outline.

Before writing your essay, develop an outline to organize the main ideas and supporting details.

> ### Ways to Organize a Literary Analysis
>
> - **Comparison/Contrast:** describe all similarities/ differences of one text and then the other; or, describe one similarity shared by both texts and then one difference between the two texts
>
> - **Summaries, Plot Analysis, Character Analysis:** explain examples in chronological order
>
> - **Analysis of Word Choice or Theme:** organize examples in order of importance (usually least to most important)

Activity 3D Analyzing an Outline

Use work you have done for previous activities to help you complete the following outline for a literary analysis essay about "The Open Window."

1. Fill in the thesis statement at the beginning and also under point B of I. Introduction.

2. Fill in subpoints 1 and 2 under points A, B, and C of II. Body.

3. Restate the thesis statement under point B of III. Conclusion.

Sample Outline: Things Aren't Always What They Seem

Thesis Statement:

_____

_____

I. Introduction
   A. Things are not always what they seem.
   B. _____

   _____

II. Body
   A. Since the events are described from Framton's
      viewpoint, Vera's story seems genuine.
      1. _____

      _____

      2. _____

      _____

   B. Because of Vera's story, it looks as though Mrs.
      Sappleton is suffering from delusions related to
      her grief.
      1. _____

      _____

      2. _____

      _____

   C. In the last part of the story, the point of view
      shifts and the reader learns the truth.
      1. _____

      _____

      2. _____

      _____

III. Conclusion
   A. Readers would have read the story differently if
      they had known earlier about the trick Vera was
      playing.
   B. _____

   _____

> **Including Textual Evidence**
>
> The body of your outline should include specific evidence from the text(s). Evidence may include direct quotations enclosed in quotation marks or paraphrases of the text.

Step 6. Write the draft.

Because you've taken good notes and developed a complete outline, writing your essay will not be difficult. Simply add a few more details to your basic outline. You will also want to include good transitional words and phrases so that the writing flows logically. The following essay contains mistakes that you will correct later in the chapter.

Activity 3E Analyzing a Model Essay

The model essay contains errors you will correct in a later activity. As you read the essay, complete the following tasks:

1. Underline the thesis statement in the introduction.

2. In the body of the essay, place a check in the margin beside three specific pieces of evidence from the story.

3. Underline two transitional phrases.

4. Identify the conclusion in the margin.

Citations in Literary Analysis

In some literary analysis assignments, you will need to identify outside sources in your text. For examples citations, see Chapter 4, Lesson 4, "Citations and Quotations," pages 57–58.

In literary analysis, all of the citations may come from one text. If so, only the page number is needed. If the work is short, such as a one-page poem, no citation may be needed at all. For longer poems include the line or page number in parentheses (e.g.,11–12).

Sample Draft: Things Aren't Always What They Seem

Things are not always what they seem. This is certainly true in "The Open Window" by Saki. The events are told by a third-person limited omniscient narrator. A man named Framton with a nervous condition. Because readers share Framton's point of view, they are deceived along with Framton by Vera's tale—a made-up story that creates a contrast between appearances and reality.

From the beginning, the narrator focuses on Framton, who has come to meet the Sappleton family. Framton is visiting the country as a "nerve cure." He is apprehensive about meeting new people and wonders if Mrs. Sappleton is nice.

To the reader, Vera's actions in the first part of the story seem genuine. When Vera asks Framton, "Do you know many of the people around here?" and "Then you know practically nothing about my aunt?" it appears as though she is making polite conversation. Neither Framton nor the reader knows the truth. That she is lying the groundwork for the story she tells. As a result, Vera's story leads Framton (and the

---

Verb Tense in Literary Analysis

It is customary in literary analysis essays to use present tense, not past tense, when describing events and characters. The reason for using the present tense is that the events in stories happen again and again each time people read them.

Example: In "The Open Window," Vera tricks Framton into believing a false story.

Not: In "The Open Window," Vera tricked Framton into believing a false story.

---

continued on next page

continued from previous page

reader) to believe that the window in the room is open because Mrs. Sappleton can't accept that her husband and brother died three years ago on a hunting excursion. It also contributes to the structure of the larger story, giving it a story-within-a-story format. Vera says "Poor aunt always thinks that they will come back someday . . . and walk in at that window just as they used to do. That is why the window is kept open every evening till it is quite dusk".

The made-up story Vera tells makes the subsequant events in the larger story appear to be other than what they are. When Mrs. Sappleton finally enters the room and begins speaking, Framton and the reader think she is suffering from delusions related to her grief. Mrs. Sappleton talks about the three men, whom Vera has said are dead, as if they are still alive and stares at the open window, waiting for them to return. Framton finds Mrs. Sappleton's talk "purely horrible" since he thinks the men are dead and makes "a desperate but only partially successful effort to turn the talk on to a less ghastly topic." He shivers when Mrs. Sappleton cries, "Here they are at last!" and turns toward Vera "with a look intended to convey sympathetic comprehension" for what he believes to be her aunt's hallucination.

At this point in the story, the narrator continues to follow Framton's point of view—but not for long. Vera continues to spin the story by expressing a look of "dazed horror" as she stares out the window at what seem to be ghosts. When Framton turns and glimpses the figures himself, he breaks down and flees. When the "ghosts" speak, the reader realizes that Vera is lying. Suspicions are further confirmed when Vera quickly makes up a second lie explaining Mr. Nuttel's hasty retreat. However, with the final line of the story the point of view shifts and we understand that Vera has a talent for telling wild stories on the fly. "Romance at short notice was her speciality."

If the third-person limited narrator had clued in readers earlier about the trick Vera was playing, the story would have been way different. Saki uses third-person limited perspective to create irony. Poor Framton came to the country to rest and instead is scared by a young girl. Ironically, the reader is also fooled along with Framton. This emphasizes the contrast between what appears to be true and what is actually true, adding depth and interest to the story.

Step 7. Revise your essay.

After you write a draft, revise it to make the content more specific, the ideas more clear, and the writing flow more smoothly. Also make sure you have included evidence to support each conclusion you have drawn about the text. Notice how the conclusion in the first sentence below is supported by evidence from the text in the second sentence.

> Since the narrator focuses on Framton's viewpoint, Vera's actions in the first part of the story seem genuine. When <u>Vera asks Framton, "Do you know many of the people around here?" and "Then you know practically nothing about my aunt?" it appears as though she is making polite conversation.</u>

Evidence to support your conclusions may include direct quotations enclosed in quotation marks or paraphrases of the text. Study the following examples:

Conclusion: Because of Vera's story, when Mrs. Sappleton finally enters the room and begins speaking, Framton and the reader think she is suffering from delusions related to her grief.

Evidence: Paraphrase of Events—Mrs. Sappleton talks about the three men, whom Vera has stated are dead, as if they are still alive and stares at the open window, waiting for them to return.

Evidence: Paraphrase with Direct Quotations—Framton finds Mrs. Sappleton's talk "purely horrible" since he thinks the men are dead and makes "a desperate but only partially successful effort to turn the talk on to a less ghastly topic."

Activity 3F Using Evidence to Support Conclusions

Write one or two sentences with evidence to support the following conclusion. Your sentence(s) should support the conclusion that Framton believes the men are ghosts.

> When Framton turns and glimpses the figures himself, he believes they are ghosts.

_____

_____

_____

_____

_____

_____

Evidence from Secondary Sources

In some literary analysis essays outside of test-taking situations, you might use evidence from secondary sources in addition to evidence from the work of literature you are analyzing. Secondary sources can include the following:

- A text that discusses the historical context of the literary work

- A text that examines the author's life and how it impacted the literary work

- A text that offers another analysis of the literary work

Use intext citations whenever you include information from secondary sources in your analysis.

Activity 3G Revising the Model Essay

In the margin of the model essay, complete the following tasks.

1. Cross out a sentence in the third paragraph that doesn't fit with the main idea.

2. Add a transitional word or phrase to help the ideas flow together better.

3. Find a sentence in the last paragraph that uses informal language and rewrite it using a more formal style.

Step 8. Edit and proofread your essay.

Once you've made your final revisions to the content and the style of your essay, read it once again. This time, focus on and correct any errors in grammar, punctuation, and spelling.

For example, read the following sentences from the student model. What errors do you notice related to punctuating the quoted material?

> Vera says "Poor aunt always thinks that they will come back someday . . . and walk in at that window just as they used to do. That is why the window is kept open every evening till it is quite dusk".

The writer has made two errors. First, the quote is not introduced by a comma after the word "says." Second, the period at the end of the quote is outside the quotation marks instead of inside. The following rules will help you punctuate quoted material correctly:

- When you are quoting one or more complete sentences, introduce or follow the quote with a comma. Periods and commas at the end of quotations always go inside the quotation marks.

  Example: The narrator tells the reader in the last paragraph, "Romance at short notice was her specialty."

- Use commas to set off the words in between a divided quotation.

  Example: "You may wonder," says Vera as she begins her story, "why we keep that window wide open on an October afternoon."

- If the quoted material is not a complete sentence or part of a divided quotation, do not introduce or follow it with a comma.

  Example: After he sees the three figures approaching, Framton grabs "wildly at his stick and hat" and makes a "headlong retreat."

Revision Tips

Check the content of your essay by asking yourself the following questions:

- Does my essay have a clear thesis or central idea?

- Does each part of my essay support or explain my thesis?

- Does my writing give enough evidence to support my conclusions?

- Is my supporting evidence relevant and specific?

- Is the style and tone of my writing appropriate for the audience and purpose?

- Place question marks and exclamation points inside the quotation marks only if they are part of the quoted material.

Examples: Framton shivers when Mrs. Sappleton cries, "Here they are at last!"

Which character said, "One would think he had seen a ghost"?

- Use single quotation marks for quotes within quotes.

Example: The story begins, "'My aunt will be down presently, Mr. Nuttel,' said a very self-possessed young lady of fifteen . . ."

Activity 3H Correcting Quotations

Rewrite the sentences using correct punctuation.

1. The reader gets a glimpse into Vera's thoughts in paragraph 5, which reads "Do you know many people round here?" asked the niece, when she judged that they had had sufficient silent communion."

_____

_____

2. Mrs. Sappleton talks, "cheerfully about the shooting and the scarcity of birds," and constantly looks past Framton, "to the open window and the lawn beyond".

_____

_____

3. In the third-to-last paragraph of the story, Mrs. Sappleton's husband asks "Who was that who bolted out as we came up"?

_____

_____

> ### Collaboration on Quotations
>
> Skim through a book or other text to find three sentences that contain dialogue or quoted material. Write down the three sentences, including the quotation marks. However, leave out any other punctuation related to the quoted material, such as end punctuation marks or commas that introduce or follow the quote.

Activity 3I Proofreading an Essay

Complete the following tasks to proofread the model essay. Make your corrections in the margin next to the model.

1. Find and correct a sentence fragment.

2. Find and correct two misspelled words and a word used incorrectly.

3. Correct a wrong use of a third-person pronoun in paragraph 4.

LESSON 4 YOU TRY IT

Now it is your turn to write a literary analysis. Use the steps outlined in this chapter and listed to the right.

 ## Activity 4A *Writing a Literary Analysis*

Choose one of the following prompts and write a literary analysis using the steps outlined in this chapter. Then use the checklist to make sure your writing conforms to the Characteristics of Good Writing.

A. Comparing Poems About Death	B. Analyzing a Theme
Read "Because I Could Not Stop For Death" by Emily Dickinson and "Transfiguration" by Louisa May Alcott. Consider how these women, who wrote during the mid-1800s, treated the topic of death. Compare and contrast their ideas about death and the style of their writing.	Choose a work of literature you have read recently and write an essay analyzing how two or more central themes of the work develop over the course of the text. Consider how the themes build upon each and what this adds to the complexity of the work.

Steps for Writing a Literary Analysis

1. Understand the prompt.
2. Take notes on the sources.
3. Write a thesis statement.
4. Organize your ideas.
5. Develop a complete outline.
6. Write the draft.
7. Revise your essay.
8. Edit and proofread your essay.

Use the following checklist to edit your essay.

My writing has . . .	
DEVELOPMENT	❏ a clear thesis statement ❏ strong supporting points ❏ addressed all the requirements of the prompt
ORGANIZATION	❏ a clear introduction, body, and conclusion ❏ good transitions ❏ logical order
EVIDENCE	❏ strong, relevant textual evidence ❏ direct quotations or paraphrased information from other texts
LANGUAGE & STYLE	❏ precise, appropriate word choice ❏ a formal, objective tone
GRAMMAR, SPELLING, & PUNCTUATION	❏ standard grammar ❏ correct spelling ❏ proper punctuation

······· **Chapter 6** ·······
Writing a Narrative

A **narrative** is a text that tells a story. The story can be either true or imagined, but it is always based on a problem, a situation, or an observation.

LESSON 1 POINT OF VIEW

Narratives come in many forms. Scientists, historians, journalists, and writers of fiction all use narratives to tell how something happened. Following are some examples of narratives:

- a novel such as *Things Fall Apart,* by Chinua Achebe

- a chapter in a book telling the story of Ernest Shackleton's survival in the Antarctic

- a short story you wrote about interstellar time travel

- an account of your first experience traveling alone

The person telling a story is the narrator. If the narrator participates in the events and describes what happens from his or her point of view, the story is a first-person narrative. If the narrator is not a participant, but is telling readers about other people, the story is a third-person narrative.

> **Pronoun Clues and Point of View**
>
> A first-person narrator often uses *I, we, me, us, my,* and *our.* A third-person narrator often uses *he, she, they, his, her, their,* and *them.*

Activity 1A Identifying the Point of View

Place a checkmark in the column to indicate whether each passage is written in the first person or the third person. Write one or more clue words that you used to make your choice.

Passage	First Person	Third Person	Clue Words
1. I saw her clearly, but only for a moment, as the trains paused beside each other in the station.			
2. For a moment the brightly lit trains were side by side, and she glimpsed a once-familiar face through the glass.			
3. We liked each other, but there was an underlying sense of competition.			
4. The men, hired at the same time, were both friends and rivals.			

LESSON 2 NARRATIVE TECHNIQUES

Narrative writers use a variety of techniques to describe experiences, explain why events happened, and to portray characters. For example:

- **Dialogue** consists of words spoken by characters in the story. These words are enclosed in quotation marks. Dialogue helps characters come alive for readers.

- **Description** includes specific details about people, things, and events. These details help the reader imagine what the writer is portraying.

- **Reflection** occurs when a character or the narrator thinks about and comments on what has happened. Reflection helps the readers understand how characters view events in the narrative.

- **Multiple plot lines** are different streams of events that are woven together into one story. A romance may describe the lives of two separate individuals who finally meet and fall in love.

> ### Pacing
>
> A skilled writer of narrative controls the pacing. **Pacing** is how quickly events occur in a story. In a fast-paced story, events rush by. In a slow-paced story, the writer takes more time for description and reflection. Writers often adjust the pacing as a way to control the tension in the story.

Activity 2A *Identifying Techniques*

In the margin of the following paragraph, write the following:

1. "dialogue" next to two examples of dialogue

2. "description" next to two descriptive words or phrases

3. "reflection" next to a comment showing reflection

   I was 13 when I arrived in Shinagawa, Japan, to take part in an exchange program. Bleary-eyed and grubby after 24 hours of travel, I shambled toward the welcoming reception. It was a visual delight. An array of dishes held gleaming morsels: pickled radish, rice wrapped in seaweed, paper-thin slices of raw fish. However, even if I'd been able to use chopsticks back then, I wouldn't have been able to muster much enthusiasm. Exhausted and nervous about meeting my Japanese host family, I found the food more off-putting than appealing. It was starting to dawn on me that I was half the world away from home.

   Even so, I was working hard at keeping the nerves in check. Then I made a tactical error. I thought I would go to the ladies room and wash my face, blow my nose, generally pull myself together. I opened the door——and broke down completely. The facilities consisted of a hole in the tiled floor. I was so out of my element that I couldn't even figure out how to go to the bathroom.

   I was furiously wiping away tears when I heard a voice speaking English with a crisp British accent.

   "A new place is always a bit overwhelming at first—the sights and smelling—and yes, the water closet, but you'll adapt."

   "I don't know . . . ," I blubbered as I turned to look into the face of young Japanese woman, dressed in a blue wool suit.

LESSON 3 SEQUENCE OF EVENTS

In a narrative, the order of events is key to communicating ideas.

- Presenting events in the order they occurred helps readers follow the story easily. This type of organization is called **chronological order.**

- Starting a story with a moment of intense action can be a good way to grab the attention of the readers.

- Beginning a story with the final result of a series of events encourages the reader to focus on the process that led up to the result. It can also create a sense of mystery or suspense.

- Use **flashback** to give backstory to events that are currently happening.

- **Foreshadowing** hints at events that happen later in the story.

- The ending of a story may resolve the conflicts or may leave the reader with some questions, depending upon the tone and theme of the story.

Use good transitional phrases to connect your events and keep your readers focused.

Activity 3A Analyzing an Event Sequence

Read the following passage. On the lines, explain how flashback is used to communicate an event sequence. Analyze whether you find this effective.

> Amy sets her mouth in a determined line.
>
> "Maybe you've forced the memories out of your mind, but I can't yet. I can't go forward unless I go back. Will you remember with me?" she asks.
>
> I am silent for a moment. I don't want to remember. I've spent so much time trying to forget. Even now, thinking about it hurts too much. I close my eyes. The scene still burns in the back of my mind.
>
> I see . . .
>
> Blinding lights break through the darkness. Gloved hands that pull me from the inferno that was once our house. My sister's beloved stuffed bear is trampled by heavy boots, and my brother's brown eyes are wide with terror.

_____

_____

_____

_____

_____

LESSON 4 DESCRIPTIVE LANGUAGE

When you write, choose clear, vivid words to paint a picture of experiences, events, setting, and characters.

- Use precise words and phrases rather than general ones. *Arctic blast* conveys more information than *cold wind*. Avoid boring verbs (*is, was, go*) in favor of more descriptive ones (*scrambled, transformed, scurried*).

- Use details that tell something significant about a person, thing, or event. Description of how a young girl chews on the end of her ponytail hints that she is nervous or unsure of herself.

- Use **sensory words** that appeal to the five senses: sight, hearing, taste, smell, and touch. Phrases such as *smelling of rot and garbage* or *crystalline snowflakes* evoke a sensory impression.

> ### Finding Vivid Words
> Use the thesaurus feature of your word processor to suggest fresh words you can use to replace vague words. Keep a list of new words you see in your reading or hear people say. To help you learn these new words, use them as soon as you can find a time that is appropriate.

Activity 4A Identifying Precise Words and Phrases

Return to the passage on page 92. Underline five examples of effective descriptive language.

Activity 4B Using Sensory Language

Continue the passage from page 92 by writing vivid description of what the character heard and felt during the house fire.

I hear . . .

_____

_____

_____

_____

_____

I feel . . .

_____

_____

_____

_____

_____

_____

_____

LESSON 5 CONCLUSION

Like other types of writing, a narrative ends with a conclusion. In a narrative, the conclusion typically gives the reader a sense that the story is complete. The conclusion

Collaboration About a Conclusion

If you are having trouble writing a strong conclusion, talk about it with a classmate or a parent.

- should follow from the rest of the narrative, wrapping up any loose ends

- may include personal reflections on the events in the narrative. In a personal narrative, the writer may explain how the incidents affected him personally.

In a text that is only a page or two long, the conclusion could be only a sentence. In a twenty-chapter novel, the conclusion may be the last chapter.

Activity 5A Analyzing a Conclusion

Read the following conclusion to the narrative from Activities 3A, 4A, and 4B on pages 92–93. Then answer the questions that follow.

> When I open my eyes, I am faced with the terrible reality of the here and now. My dad is gone. He died saving our lives.
>
> Most days I try not to remember the events of that horrible night. But my sister Amy who was just five years old at the time, sometimes asks me to go back there.
>
> Maybe she is right. Maybe talking about the worst day of my life will bring some healing from this festering wound. Maybe someday I'll be able to forgive myself for what happened to Dad. Maybe I won't always feel that it was my fault. Perhaps someday a scar, ugly and discolored, will form and I will be able to move on.

1. How does the conclusion explain the outcome of the fire?

_____

_____

_____

_____

_____

_____

2. In the conclusion, underline examples of how the incident affected the narrator personally.

LESSON 6 HOW TO WRITE A NARRATIVE ESSAY

Following is a model demonstrating the six steps in writing a narrative essay. Use these six steps to help you write your own essays.

Step 1. Understand the prompt.

The directions for writing a narrative essay are called the **prompt.**

Activity 6A Analyzing the Prompt

The following is a prompt for a college entrance essay. Underline the key words.

> Recount a time when you experienced failure. How did it affect you at the time? What lessons did you learn from the experience?

Step 2. Take notes.

Even though you will be writing about your own experience, it is still important to make notes and organize your ideas before starting to write.

Activity 6B Making Notes

Look back at the prompt in Activity 6A. Name the incident or event you will write about. Answer the following essential questions about the event. Then add at least three concrete details for each answer.

What was the event?

_____

_____

Who was involved?

_____

_____

_____

What happened?

_____

_____

_____

_____

_____

Researching a Narrative

When recalling events from your life, it may be helpful to ask the people involved to help you remember important details such as conversation and when events happened.

When did it happen?

_____

_____

_____

Where did it happen?

_____

_____

_____

Why was this incident important to you?

_____

_____

_____

_____

_____

_____

How did it affect you?

_____

_____

_____

_____

_____

Step 3. Organize your ideas.

Create an outline of the events in your narrative. Get the reader's attention right away. Perhaps you want to jump immediately to the high point of the action with the first line. The rest of the introduction could lead up to the thesis statement. The body expounds on the events that led up to the intense moment described in the first line. At the end of the body, express the immediate outcomes of the incident. In the conclusion, reflect on your current perspective toward the events, including how they shaped your character.

Writing a Strong College-Entrance Essay

1. Be honest. Accurately represent yourself and your accomplishments.

2. Be an individual. Think about how you can distinguish your essay from hundreds of others.

3. Be vivid. Use good details to draw the reader into the story. Details reveal your true self.

4. Be focused. You don't have time to write about every event that shaped your life. Keep the writing within the stated limits.

Activity 6C Analyzing the Outline

Complete the following as you study the outline below.

1. Write "chronological" where the events are placed in time order.

2. Write "flashback" where the writer goes back to remember previous events.

3. Write "climax" in the margin beside the place where the conflict is resolved.

4. Write "reflection" in the margin beside places where the writer reflects on how failure affected him.

> **Timelines for Narratives**
>
> For a narrative essay, you could use a timeline instead of an outline. A timeline will help you keep events in order.

Sample Outline: Facing Down Failure

I. Introduction

    A. My geometry test was sitting face down on my desk.

    B. If I did well on the test, I would pass geometry.

II. Body

    A. I was a good student involved in basketball, track, and student government, then I took geometry my sophomore year.

    B. I struggled with the concepts, but didn't ask anyone for help.

    C. My basketball coach told me that I wouldn't be able to play basketball if I didn't get my grade up.

    D. I talked to my teacher and started getting extra help.

III. Conclusion

    A. I got a B- on my test and passed the class.

    B. I learned to not be too proud to ask for help when I'm struggling.

Step 4. Write the draft.

Using your notes and your outline, write your essay. The following sample draft includes errors that you will correct in later activities.

Sample Draft: Facing Down Failure

I didn't want to look at the paper sitting face down on my desk. I feel tears coming to my eyes, but I forced them back. I wasn't going to cry in front of my entire geometry class. My geometry grade for the semester was riding on this test. If I failed this test, I failed the class.

. . .

Before my sophomore year, school had been relatively easy. I didn't have to spend much time studying outside of class. This was good because I was really busy with extracurricular activities. I played basketball and ran track for my school. I was also involved in student government. I was able to get As and Bs without much trouble.

So when I started geometry my sophomore year, I wasn't expecting how difficult it would be. Suddenly, I had to memorize theorems and use deductive reasoning to prove why angles were congruent. It was an entirely new way of thinking. I felt like I had gotten on a plane to go to Africa and landed in Iceland instead.

For a while, I was able to struggle along. I could do okay on the daily assignments. Often, I would get help from my friend Jamal, who was really smart in math. However, the tests were brutal. By mid-term I was barely passing.

Unfortunately, I was too embarrassed to ask my teacher Mr. Jackson for help. I was a good student; I'd always made the honor roll in the past. If I admitted I needed help, what would he think of me. I had to maintain my image as a "smart kid."

Then one night after practice, my basketball coach, Ms. Cooper called me over.

She said that my counselor had told her that I was failing geometry. Our school policy was that if you had

continued on next page

continued from previous page

any Fs, you couldn't play sports. I felt really ashamed. I told Coach that I thought geometry was stupid and I was trying really hard, but I just couldn't get it.

She encouraged me to talk to my teacher and put together a plan to help me pass the class. She reminded me that I needed to take geometry if I was going to go to college.

The next morning before school I talked to Mr. Jackson. He told me about a tutoring program for struggling students. I hated that word "struggling," but I swallowed my pride. I started to come in early three times a week to get extra help. I also spent twenty minutes every night reviewing my notes from class. Slowly, I began to make sense of all the terms and theorems. I learned different ways of solving problems that made sense to me. I felt like I understood the ideas better but could I perform when it really counted—on the final test?

. . .

I flipped over the paper on my desk. There in red ink was a B-. I let out the biggest whoop of joy. The entire class stared at me, but Mr. Jackson just smiled.

I can look back on that experience now and be grateful. Failing geometry was painful at the time, but I learned some important things about life. Difficult times are going to come. I will face failure again. However, now I am more open to asking for help, instead of struggling along on my own. There are people who will help you, if you aren't too proud to admit that you need help.

In my locker at school, I have a quote from Winston Churchill. "Success is not final, failure is not fatal; it is the courage to continue that counts."

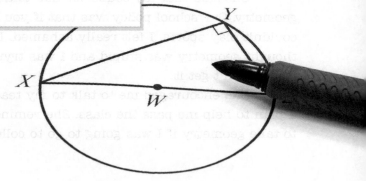

Activity 6D Evaluating the Draft

Mark the following comments on the draft on pages 98–99.

1. Circle two transition words that connect sentences effectively.

2. Underline three examples of descriptive words or phrases.

3. Do you find the order of events effective or confusing? If you do, place a ? beside any confusing sections.

4. Where could dialogue be used to make the writing more interesting? Write the word "dialogue" in the margin.

Step 5. Revise your narrative.

After you write a draft, read it again carefully. Make revisions to improve the effectiveness of the writing. When writing a personal narrative, don't shy away from including dialogue. You will probably not remember every word in the conversation, but reproduce it as closely as you can. Consider how dialogue makes the following narrative more interesting.

> Mr. Jackson held my test paper in his hand. I couldn't read the grade. He raised his bushy eyebrows.
>
> "Do you want to guess how you did?" he asked flatly.
>
> My palms were sweating and my heart felt like it was going to jump out of my body.
>
> "Did I get an F?" I managed to squeak out.
>
> "No." The corner of his mouth twitched upward, and I began to hope.

Notice how the lines in between the dialogue communicate facial expression and emotion. Also use speaker tags to indicate how a person says the words (*he growled, she sighed*).

Activity 6E Adding Dialogue to Narrative

Reread the following section of the narrative.

> Then one night after practice, my basketball coach, Ms. Cooper called me over.
>
> She said that my counselor had told her that I was failing geometry. Our school policy was that if you had any Fs, you couldn't play sports. I felt really ashamed. I told Coach that I thought geometry was stupid and I was trying really hard, but I just couldn't get it.
>
> She encouraged me to talk to my teacher and put together a plan to help me pass the class. She reminded me that I needed to take geometry if I was going to go to college.

Below is a revision of the paragraphs on the bottom of page 100. Notice that interesting dialogue has been added. Finish the rest of the revision. Punctuate dialogue correctly.

     Then one night after practice, my basketball coach, Ms. Cooper called me over.

     "Jada, your counselor just told me that you are getting an F in geometry. You know our academic policy. If you are failing a class, you can't play sports." Ms. Cooper looked at me sternly. "This isn't like you, Jada. What's going on?"

     I was so ashamed and angry, I couldn't look Coach Cooper in the eye.

_____

_____

_____

_____

_____

_____

_____

_____

_____

_____

_____

_____

_____

_____

_____

_____

_____

Step 6. Edit and proofread your narrative.

After you write a draft, read it again carefully, checking for mistakes in spelling, punctuation, grammar, and usage. When writing a narrative, verb tenses are very important. When writing about events that happened in the past, use past tense. Use past perfect tense to communicate events that were completed before current time. Study the underlined verbs in the following sentence.

> I <u>didn't</u> <u>want</u> to look at the paper sitting face down on my desk. I <u>feel</u> tears coming to my eyes, but I <u>forced</u> them back.

The verbs *did want* and *forced* indicate that the action is taking place in past tense. However, *feel* is a present tense verb; change *feel* to *felt* to keep the verb tenses consistent.

Use past perfect tense (had + past participle) to indicate events that happened before that of another past tense.

> Before my sophomore year, school <u>had been</u> relatively easy. I <u>didn't</u> <u>have</u> to spend much time studying.

Activity 6F Using Correct Verb Tenses

Underline the verbs that are in the wrong tense. Write the correct verb on the lines.

1. I graduated from high school last spring, then I take a trip to Europe right after that.

_____

2. During class the professor explains the concepts to students who asked questions.

_____

3. Before this year, I have enough credits to graduate.

_____

4. I did well on the exam because I have studied the night before.

_____

5. I never rode a horse before today.

_____

> ### Correct Spelling
>
> About 80 percent of words in English follow regular spelling rules. Learning these rules, then, can help you spell most words. Only about 300 English words are truly difficult for most people to spell. This is a small enough number that you can study and master them.

LESSON 7 YOU TRY IT

Now it is your turn to write a narrative. Use the steps outlined in this chapter and listed to the right.

Activity 7A *Writing a Narrative*

Choose one of the following prompts and write a narrative in response to it.

Writing a Narrative Essay

1. Understand the prompt.
2. Take notes on sources.
3. Organize your ideas.
4. Write the draft.
5. Revise your narrative.
6. Edit and proofread your narrative.

A. Writing a Historical Narrative	B. Writing Documentation
Read several sources about the 1957 desegregation of Central High School in Little Rock, Arkansas. Carefully and accurately describe the events and main characters based upon the sources provided. Use good details from the sources in your narrative.	Many jobs require workers to document incidents or interactions between clients and employees. Choose a recent incident that happened either at work or at school. Write a detailed narrative of the event. Include the actions and reactions of the people involved. Try to be as objective as possible.

My writing has . . .	
DEVELOPMENT	❏ a clear experience or event to tell ❏ narrative techniques to develop experiences, events, and characters
ORGANIZATION	❏ a problem, situation, or observation to engage the reader ❏ a clear introduction, body, and conclusion ❏ good transitions to maintain the flow of ideas ❏ events that build on one another to create a coherent whole
EVIDENCE	❏ well-chosen details ❏ well-structured event sequences
LANGUAGE & STYLE	❏ precise words and phrases ❏ telling details ❏ sensory language
GRAMMAR, SPELLING, & PUNCTUATION	❏ standard grammar ❏ correct spelling ❏ proper punctuation

Tips for Success

LESSON 1 WRITING TEST TIPS

When the day of your test arrives, make sure you're prepared to show what you know. The following tips will help you do your best on writing tests.

☐ 1. What you do before the test affects how you do on the test. Get a good night's sleep, eat a good breakfast (or lunch, depending on when you take the test), and use the restroom before the test begins. Keep your nerves under control by taking a few deep breaths before you begin. Think positively.

☐ 2. It's likely that you won't know what the prompts are before the test period begins. So begin the test by quickly previewing all the prompts. This will tell you what the test is about and how many texts you will write.

☐ 3. Read each prompt carefully. Locate key words or phrases that will help you understand what you need to write. If you misread the prompt, you will get a low score no matter how brilliantly you write.

☐ 4. Confirm the amount of time you have to write, and then plan your time accordingly. Allow a few minutes at the beginning of each task for prewriting and a few minutes at the end for revising. Use most of the time for writing. Monitor your time, allowing enough time to write, revise, and proofread.

☐ 5. As you respond to each prompt, brainstorm your thoughts about the topic. If helpful, use graphic organizers or outlines to organize main ideas.

☐ 6. If your essay is written by hand, write neatly. You won't get a good score if the grader can't read your writing.

Types of Main Ideas

Depending on the type of essay you are writing your main idea might be a

- claim to support
- topic to examine
- situation to explain
- problem to solve
- question to answer

Activity 1A Applying the Tips

Read the following prompt and respond to the questions that follow it.

Many articles have been written in recent years about the phenomenon of "helicopter parents" who are perceived to "hover" over their children even after their children have left home for college. They call professors to complain about grades, they call landlords to mediate disputes, and they otherwise try to fix problems their children encounter. Critics of helicopter parenting say that it keeps young people from growing up and handling their own difficulties. Defenders say that parental responsibility doesn't end when young people leave home, and that young people who are "helicopter parented" are happier in college than those who are not.

What do you think? Is "helicopter parenting" good for young people, or bad? In your essay, take a position on this question. Support your position with reasons and examples from your own experience.

1. In this prompt, what type of essay are you being asked to write?

   A. informative

   B. narrative

   C. argumentative

   D. literary analysis

2. How do you know that your answer to Question 1 is correct?

   _____

   _____

   _____

   _____

   _____

   _____

   _____

LESSON 2 TIPS FOR REVISION

You may not have much time to revise an essay on a test. As a result, you will want to decide quickly what to fix. Here is a list of actions to take.

☐ 1. Reread your main idea carefully. It should be stated precisely and clearly.

☐ 2. Compare your introduction and your conclusion. They should both address the main idea.

☐ 3. Be sure your body paragraphs have enough details, such as relevant evidence, well-chosen facts, precise words, and sensory language.

☐ 4. Check for appropriate and varied transitions between paragraphs and between sentences.

☐ 5. Read your essay silently, but slowly, word-by-word, as if you were giving a speech. Revise any awkward words or phrases.

☐ 6. Look for words you might have omitted or written twice.

☐ 7. Check the style and tone of the essay. Usually, you should use a formal style and objective tone.

☐ 8. Check that each pronoun refers clearly to a noun and is used correctly.

☐ 9. Insert commas where needed. Delete commas where they are not.

☐ 10. Correct any misspelled words. If you are writing your essay on a computer, some of these may be highlighted by the word processing program.

Corrections by Hand

If you are writing your essay by hand, make any changes neatly. Use a caret (^) to indicate where you are inserting text.

Finish Writing Before You Edit

Plan to save time to revise your writing. However, don't stop writing to revise. Finishing all tasks is more important than revising any single one.

Activity 2A Applying Revision Tips

Below is a draft of an informational essay about Franklin D. Roosevelt. It contains at least 18 errors. Underline each error that you find and then correct it in the margin to the right.

When Franklin D. Roosevelt was 39 years old. He lost the use of his legs due to polio. 4 days after falling ill on vacation in Canada in 1921, he was paralyzed from the chest down. Although his condition improved somewhat over a period of weeks, he would remain perminently paralyzed from the waist down.

Roosevelt never believed that his condition was permanint, and he persuaded many people of this belief. It was necessary of he was to continue his political career. He had run unsuccessfully for vice-president in 1920, although he did not hold public office when he became ill, he hoped to return to it. In 1928 he did, winning the office of governor in the state of New York. At that time, many people considered a physical disability to be disturbing at best and shameful at worse. The thinking was that the disabled could never be productive members of society. Roosevelt believed it would be seen as a sign of weakness. It was pretty silly of people to think that way, wasn't it?

Roosevelt won the presidency in 1932. Although Roosevelt used a wheelchair during his entire time in offie, he was never seen with it in public, and only few photographs exist of him sitting in it. Franklin learned to walk convincingly enough by supporting himself with a cane and using his torso to pull his legs around, in fact it was an extremely difficult process. He occasionally used crutches. Whenever he had to stand, he wore leg braces, and when: he gave a speech, the lectern at which he stood had to be sturdy enough for him to lean on.

Controversially, the FDR Memorial in Washington opened with a statue of a seated FDR who was having a cape cover his wheelchair. Activists for the disabled objected. And and they raised money for another statue, this one depicts botn the former president and his wheelchair. It serves as a reminder to all Americans that a physical disability need not keep anyone from achieving greatness in whatever field they chose.

LESSON 3 TIPS FOR SPEAKING AND LISTENING

Like reading, listening is a way to gather information. Like writing, speaking is a way to share what you know and think. The following list of tips will help you speak and listen effectively.

☐ 1. Prepare for a discussion by planning what you want to say. Know the evidence you want to refer to that supports your point.

☐ 2. Follow the rules of the discussion. Understand how often you should speak and how long you can speak.

☐ 3. Ask specific questions of other individuals in the discussion. Answer questions asked of you.

☐ 4. Review key ideas. Reflect on what they mean and practice paraphrasing them.

☐ 5. Identify a speaker's claims. Distinguish those that are supported by reasons and evidence and those that are not.

☐ 6. Interpret any images, graphics, or music that a speaker uses.

☐ 7. When presenting your idea orally, use appropriate eye contact, adequate volume, and clear pronunciation.

☐ 8. Use multimedia components, such as graphics, images, music, and sound, in your presentation.

☐ 9. Adapt your presentation to the context and the task.

> ## Evaluating Speaking and Listening Skills
>
> To become more familiar with the tips presented on this page, apply them to discussions held by others. Listen to a panel discussion on a television show. Evaluate how well the participants followed the tips.

Activity 3A Engaging in Discussion

Participate in a small group discussion about a topic about which you have or can gather much solid information. When your group is done, answer these questions about your discussion.

1. How well did members of the group refer to evidence on the topic?

_____

_____

2. How polite were members of the group toward each other?

_____

_____

3. How well did members of the group ask and respond to specific questions raised in the discussion?

_____

_____

_____

Activity 3B Interpreting Speeches

Take notes as you listen to a video of a speech or lecture on the Internet that presents an argument. Then answer the following questions about what you heard.

1. What was the speaker's argument? Identify the specific claims made by the speaker.

_____

_____

_____

_____

_____

2. What reasons and evidence did the speaker provide to support his or her claims?

_____

_____

_____

_____

_____

_____

_____

_____

_____

_____

Collaboration on Speaking and Listening

Practice your speaking and listening skills with a partner. Discuss a topic of mutual interest for two minutes. Then summarize what the other person has said. Check that each of you has spoken your ideas clearly and has listened accurately.

3. Explain whether you think the reasons and evidence supported the specific claims strongly or not.

_____

_____

_____

_____

Activity 3C _Practicing a Speech_

Have a friend videotape you as you present a one-minute excerpt from a famous speech. Review the videotape together and evaluate your speech on these issues:

1. Did you use appropriate eye contact? Explain.

_____

_____

_____

_____

2. Did you speak loudly enough to be heard easily? Explain.

_____

_____

_____

_____

3. Was your pronunciation clear? Explain.

_____

_____

_____

_____

········· **Notes** ·············

Notes